PUZZLES FOR THE SMALL ROOM

Parragon
Bath • New York • Cologne • Melbourne • Delhi
Hong Kong • Shenzhen • Singapore • Amsterdam

This edition published by Parragon Books Ltd in 2014

Parragon Books Ltd
Chartist House
15–17 Trim Street
Bath BA1 1HA, UK
www.parragon.com

ISBN 978-1-4723-5919-3

Printed in China

Crossword

Across

6 Boundary shrubs (5)
7 Badly (6)
9 Reveal (7)
10 Tests (5)
11 Consumes (4)
13 Put in (6)
15 Appears (5)
16 Eccentric person (3,3)
17 Pain (4)
20 Evade (5)
22 Tedium (7)
23 A single pen move (6)
24 Wall section (5)

Down

1 Learned (8)
2 Nothings (5)
3 Barb (5)
4 Rules (7)
5 Appeal (4)
6 Homes (10)
8 At the same temperature (10)
12 Ate (3)
13 Small devil (3)
14 Encryption (8)

15 Via unknown means (7)
18 Monks' building (5)
19 Ensnares (5)
21 Companion (4)

Gone Snorkelling

Find each of the listed items in this wordsearch puzzle. They can be written forwards or backwards in any direction, including diagonally.

BARRIER REEF
BUBBLES
CORAL
CURRENT
FLIPPERS
FLOATING
ISLANDS
MASK
MOLLUSCS
OCEAN
ROCKS
SEA GRASS
SEAWEED
SHIPWRECK
SNORKEL
STINGRAYS
SWIMMING
TIDE
TROPICAL FISH
WAVES

A	I	T	I	U	O	R	S	M	R	F	A	M	O	O	S	S
U	V	B	K	I	T	E	O	W	O	W	S	M	N	N	N	E
R	C	U	N	G	N	I	T	A	O	L	F	A	T	E	C	O
V	H	B	K	W	E	O	D	V	M	W	L	L	C	A	K	B
P	F	B	O	B	R	A	N	E	O	S	O	U	O	I	K	B
D	R	L	E	K	R	O	N	S	R	O	C	K	S	A	M	E
E	N	E	I	O	U	E	F	W	B	K	E	S	S	C	L	S
L	L	S	G	P	C	M	E	A	C	G	A	D	T	W	S	A
D	B	K	W	C	P	O	E	E	T	R	N	F	E	D	T	N
L	P	E	A	I	G	E	R	N	G	A	G	H	E	E	I	B
K	F	N	O	T	M	W	R	A	L	C	M	E	S	E	N	F
W	S	I	L	Y	P	M	E	S	L	I	W	E	W	N	G	T
B	E	O	C	I	H	S	I	F	L	A	C	I	P	O	R	T
C	F	O	H	W	E	M	R	N	E	N	O	N	O	L	A	A
S	I	S	A	C	W	A	R	S	G	T	T	L	Y	O	Y	E
G	S	S	H	O	A	I	A	F	O	R	A	A	V	N	S	D
D	E	S	T	R	C	M	B	K	S	B	O	I	N	T	R	N

Jigsaw Sudoku

Place 1 to 9 once each into every row, column and bold-lined jigsaw shape of this puzzle.

		2	5				4	
			3	5				2
9						8		
				1	2			
			4		1			
			8	4				
		7						9
1				3	4			
	3				9	7		

Going Round in Circles

Can you find a path through the maze, entering at the top and exiting at the bottom?

Number Link

Draw horizontal and vertical lines to form a set of paths, each connecting a pair of identical numbers. All numbers must be used. No more than one line can pass through any square.

1				2	3		4		
5			6					7	
				2	6	8			
			1						
		5	8						
						9			
						10			
	11	12							
3						7			
12		11		10		9	4		

Calcudoku

Place 1 to 8 once each into every row and column, while obeying the clues. The value at the top left of each bold-lined region must result when the numbers in that region have the given operation (+, -, ×, ÷) applied between them. For - and ÷ operations, start with the largest number in the region and then subtract or divide by the remaining numbers.

12+		20×	4−		1008×		
12×				4−		15×	
	144×				11+		6÷
72×			70×			1−	
12+		18+					
	4÷		4÷	72×			7+
8×		210×		72×	35×	1−	

Bridges

Join circled numbers with horizontal or vertical lines so that each number has the given number of connecting lines. No more than two lines may join any pair of numbers, and lines cannot cross. The finished layout must allow you to travel from any number to any other number just by following one or more lines.

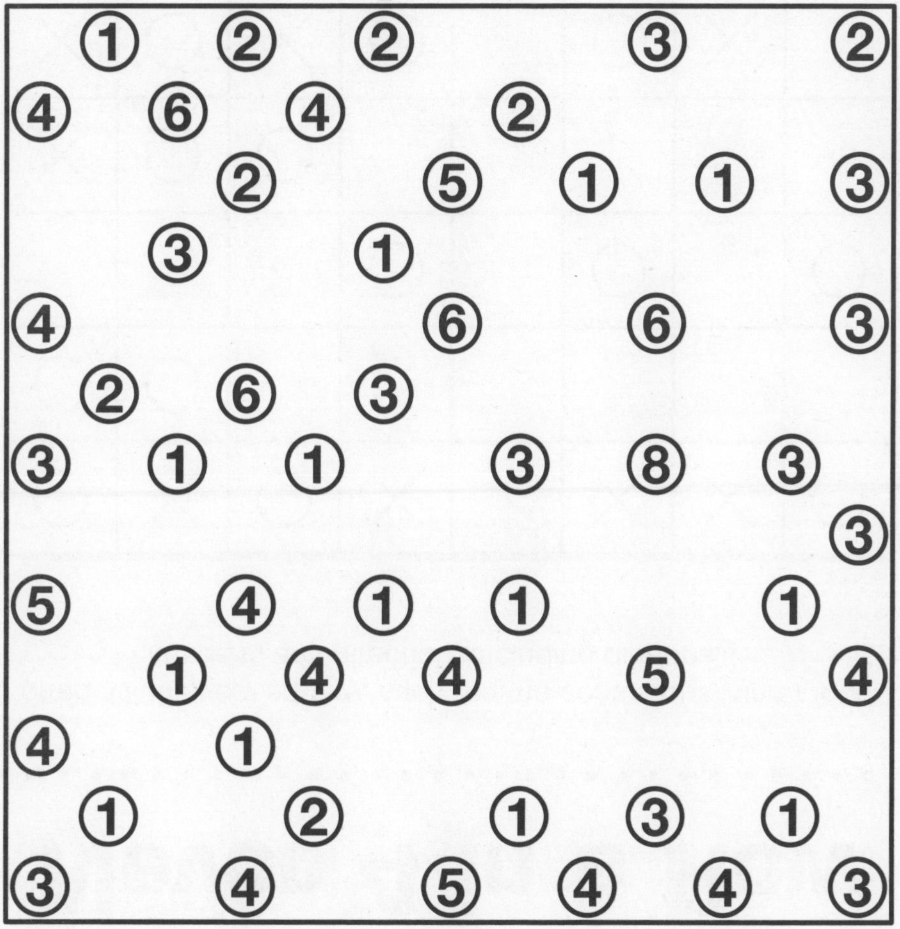

Never 4 in a Row

Place an 'X' or an 'O' in every square, such that no continuous line of four 'X's or 'O's is made in any direction, including diagonally.

O	X	O	X		X	X	O
O	O						
			O		O		O
X	O	O					
X	O	X	O		O	X	
	O			O		X	X
		X		X			O
O	O		O			X	O

Slitherlink

Draw a single loop by connecting dots with horizontal and vertical lines so that each numbered square has the specified number of adjacent line segments. The loop cannot cross or touch itself at any point.

			3		2	3	
3		2		3			1
3		2		1		3	
2		3	1			1	2
3	3			3	2		3
	2		3		2		2
3			2		3		3
	1	2		2			

Codeword

Each number in this grid represents a different letter. Solve the code to create a complete crossword grid, using only English words (no proper nouns or abbreviations).

You can use the table beneath the grid to keep track of the code, and can cross off used letters along both sides of the grid.

A	■	7	12	1	24	7	13	26	■	7	24	3	12	N
B	20	■	5	■	11	■	9 I	■	■	12	■	12	■	O
C	24	1	8	15 U	22	■	26	12	7	14	12 E	7	26	P
D	4	■	10	■	4	■	19	■	12	■	■	10	■	Q
E	11	24	7	26	■	21	15	9	19	2	12	26	6	R
F	12	■	19	■	11	■	26	■	12	■	23	■	■	S
G	■	14	9	7	15	26	■	26	5	24	19	2	■	T
H	■	■	5	■	6	■	12	■	6	■	12	■	25	U
I	5	12	18	24	6	9	14	12	■	19	22	15	12	V
J	■	20	■	■	12	■	10	■	1	■	22	■	24	W
K	24	17	17	24	7	12	22	■	24	20	12	5	13	X
L	■	6	■	1	■	■	14	■	14	■	5	■	26	Y
M	11	4	6	12	■	7	12	16	12	19	6	26	■	Z

1	2	3	4	5	6	7	8	9	10	11	12	13
14	15	16	17	18	19	20	21	22	23	24	25	26

Rectangles

Draw rectangles along the grid lines so that each number ends up in a rectangle containing exactly that many cells. Each cell must be in exactly one rectangle – so rectangles cannot overlap.

6				4				2	
				15					
9			4						
				2					5
	3			2	6				
								5	
									4
							24		
		9							

Kakuro

Place a number in the range 1–9 into every white cell, so that every horizontal run of white cells adds up to the number given to its left, and every vertical run of white cells adds up to the number given above it. No number can be repeated within a run.

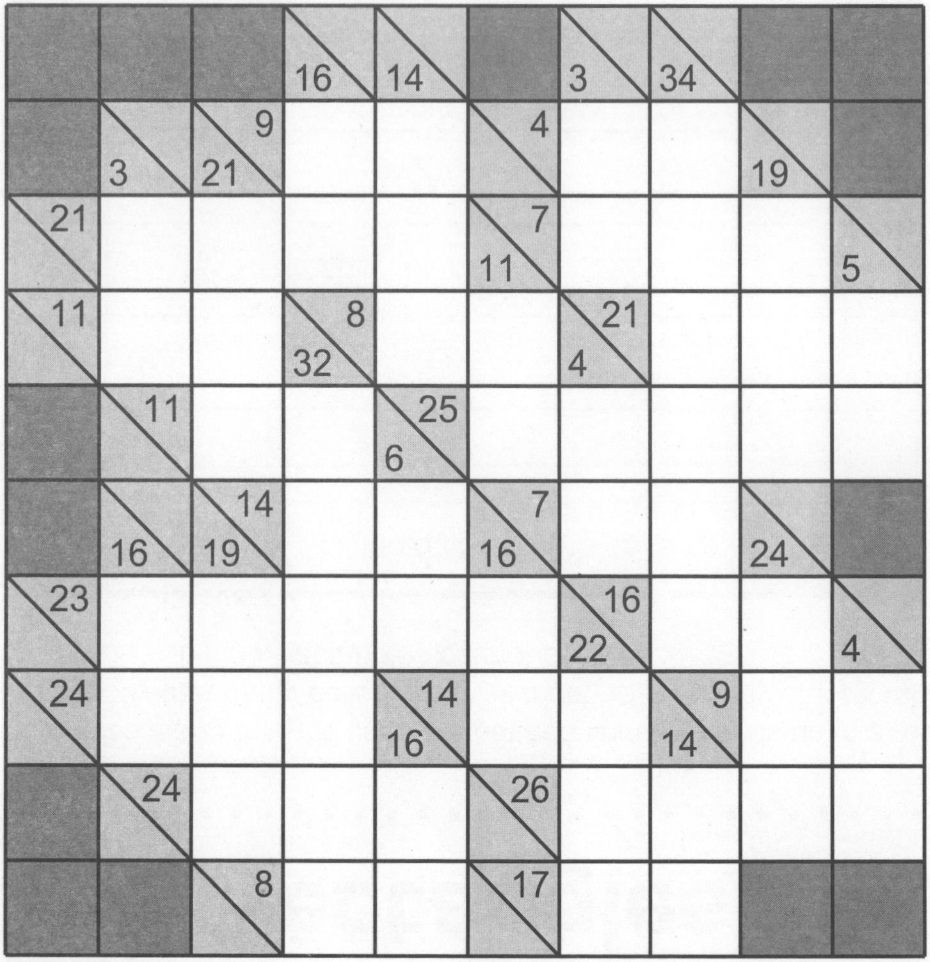

Futoshiki

Place 1 to 8 once each into every row and column while obeying the inequality signs. Less than ('<') and greater than ('>') signs between some squares indicate that the values in these two squares must be greater than, or less than, one another, as indicated by the sign.

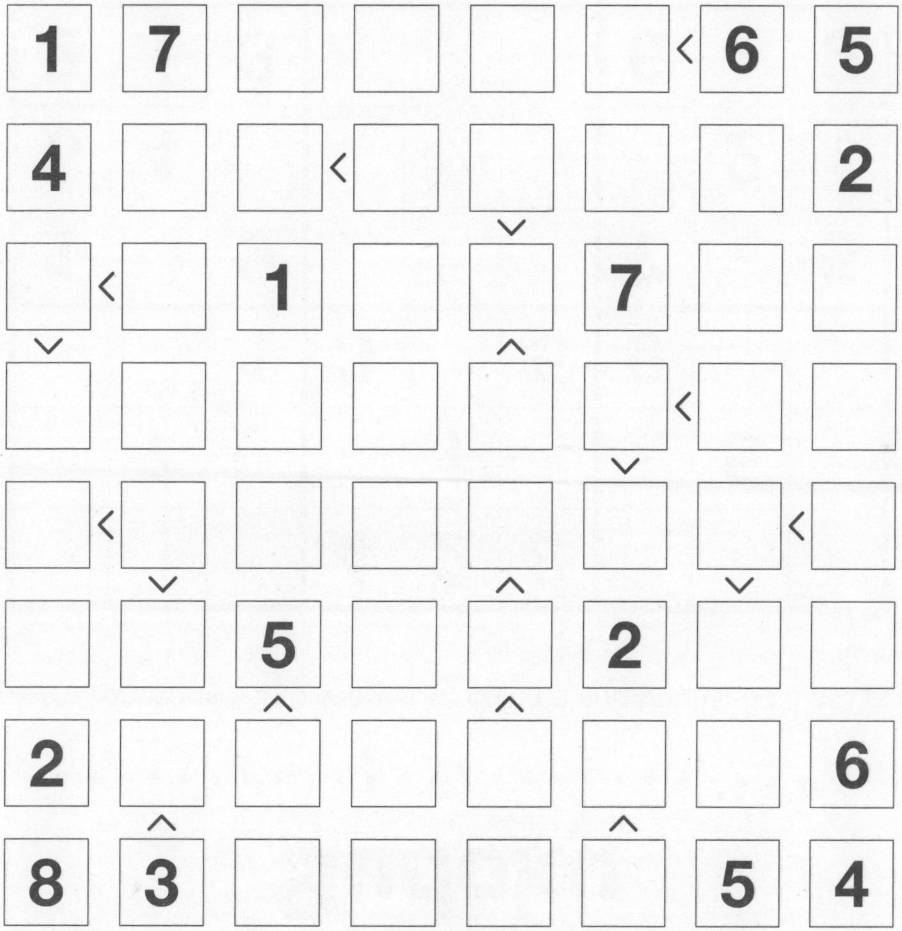

Sudoku

Place 1 to 9 once each into every row, column and bold-lined 3 × 3 square.

			4	2	8			
	7			1			5	
		1	3		5	9		
1		9				7		5
6	4						2	1
2		3				6		9
		4	8		9	5		
	6			5			8	
			2	3	7			

Letter Circle

Can you find the nine-letter word hidden in this Letter Circle? Form words by using the centre letter and a combination of two or more other letters from the circle. How many other words can you find?

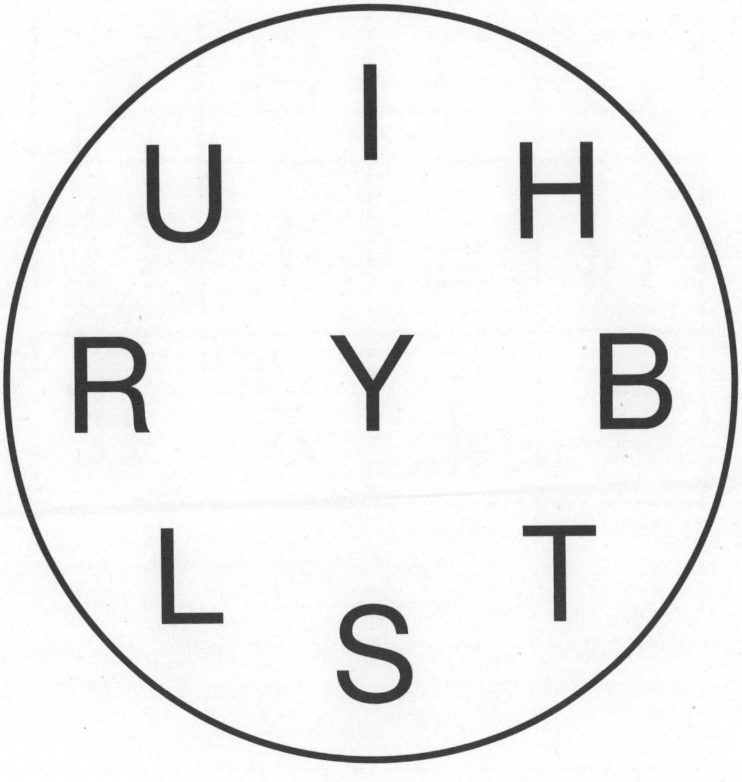

Word Square

Can you find the 16-letter word hidden in this Word Square? Find words by moving from letter to touching letter, excluding diagonally, and without revisiting a square in a single word. How many other words can you find?

E	X	T	I
N	I	E	N
A	B	L	G
H	S	I	U

Crossword

Across

1 Concentration (7)
5 Tease (4)
9 Item (7)
10 Nobles (5)
11 Audacity (5)
12 Fears (6)
14 Curved shape (6)
16 Freshest (6)
18 Option (6)
19 Artist's support (5)
22 Makes (5)
23 Most affluent (7)
24 Location (4)
25 Stored away (7)

Down

2 Consumer (5)
3 Assistants (11)
4 Chic (6)
6 Late (7)
7 Besides (4)
8 Sorrow (7)
10 Choices (11)
13 Usefulness (7)
15 Receive from your parents (7)
17 Rue (6)
20 Spectacle (5)
21 Jelly-like substances (4)

Good Hair Day?

Find each of the listed items in this wordsearch puzzle. They can be written forwards or backwards in any direction, including diagonally.

BOBBLE
BRUSH
CLIP
COMB
CONDITIONER
CRIMPERS
CURLERS
DYE
HAIRBAND
HAIRDRYER
HAIRGRIP
HAIRPIN
MOUSSE
RAZOR
SALT SPRAY
SCISSORS
SHAMPOO
STRAIGHTENERS
STYLING WAX
VOLUMIZER

S	I	R	I	M	M	B	G	A	I	I	D	D	R	L	R	M
R	A	C	W	A	O	E	H	O	I	H	A	P	S	A	V	A
H	B	P	S	M	A	I	L	I	P	I	B	T	S	S	I	Z
P	I	L	C	R	X	B	E	A	H	I	Y	W	H	L	E	E
C	H	A	I	R	B	A	N	D	S	C	B	G	O	Y	U	O
R	L	S	S	P	C	B	W	P	I	R	G	R	I	A	H	R
I	E	M	S	T	R	A	I	G	H	T	E	N	E	R	S	S
M	Y	Y	O	A	M	E	B	H	N	N	N	S	A	P	T	P
P	U	L	R	U	Y	X	Z	A	O	I	I	H	R	S	C	A
E	A	R	S	D	S	E	U	I	S	H	L	T	B	T	S	I
R	P	A	H	H	R	S	T	S	M	S	A	Y	E	L	B	B
S	R	P	A	T	M	I	E	C	P	U	R	I	T	A	I	A
I	S	U	M	R	D	L	A	C	U	R	L	E	R	S	A	I
D	B	N	P	N	B	E	T	H	U	B	C	O	H	P	R	Y
C	W	E	O	B	R	T	B	Y	L	R	Z	O	V	H	I	R
L	S	C	O	M	B	M	T	H	S	A	A	T	B	I	I	N
N	R	B	C	G	A	E	A	T	R	I	I	O	G	O	N	R

Jigsaw Sudoku

Place 1 to 9 once each into every row, column and bold-lined jigsaw shape of this puzzle.

	5				6			8
	6			1	7			
5			1					
	9			3				
				9			7	
					8			3
			2	6			3	
1			7				2	

Going Round in Circles

Can you find a path through the maze, entering at the top and exiting at the bottom?

Number Link

Draw horizontal and vertical lines to form a set of paths, each connecting a pair of identical numbers. All numbers must be used. No more than one line can pass through any square.

						1			
	2					2	3	4	
5	6	5		7		8	1		
							9	4	
							10		3
						11			
	6					9	8		10
				7					11

Calcudoku

Place 1 to 8 once each into every row and column, while obeying the clues. The value at the top left of each bold-lined region must result when the numbers in that region have the given operation (+, -, ×, ÷) applied between them. For - and ÷ operations, start with the largest number in the region and then subtract or divide by the remaining numbers.

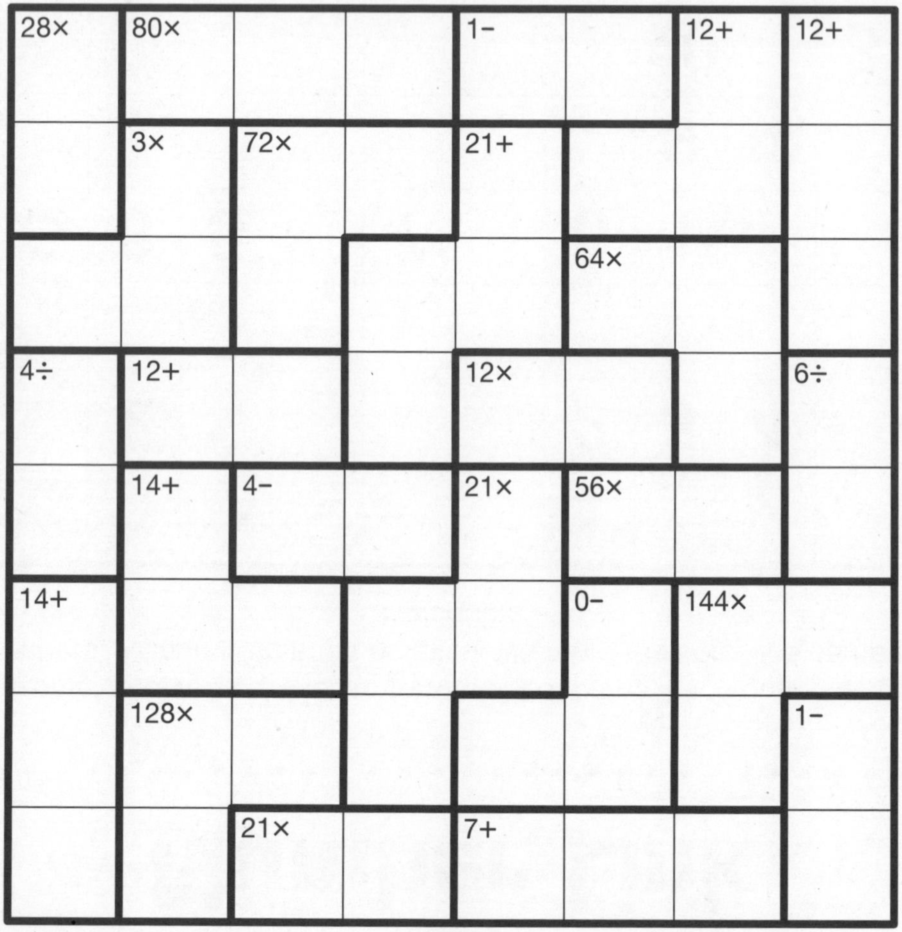

Bridges

Join circled numbers with horizontal or vertical lines so that each number has the given number of connecting lines. No more than two lines may join any pair of numbers, and lines cannot cross. The finished layout must allow you to travel from any number to any other number just by following one or more lines.

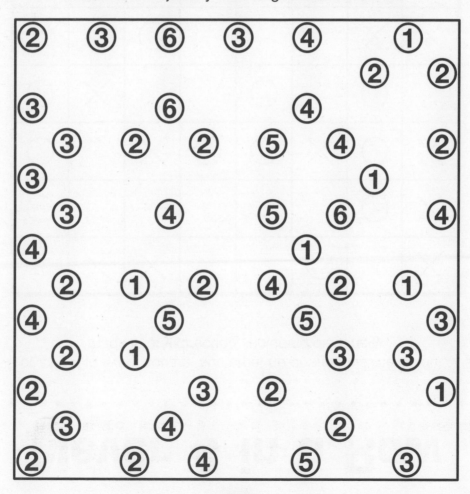

2		3		6		3		4			1	
										2		2
3				6				4				
	3		2		2		5		4			2
3										1		
	3			4			5		6			4
4								1				
	2		1		2		4		2		1	
4				5				5				3
	2		1						3		3	
2					3		2					1
	3			4					2			
2			2		4			5			3	

Never 4 in a Row

Place an ‘X’ or an ‘O’ in every square, such that no continuous line of four ‘X’s or ‘O’s is made in any direction, including diagonally.

	X	X			O		X
O						O	X
O		X	O	O	X	O	X
O	X			O		O	
		O				X	X
X	O		X	X		O	X
X	O	X		X	X		
	X	X	X		O		O

Slitherlink

Draw a single loop by connecting dots with horizontal and vertical lines so that each numbered square has the specified number of adjacent line segments. The loop cannot cross or touch itself at any point.

	2		2	2		2	
3		3		3		2	
3		2		3		2	3
	3		2				3
1				3		1	
3	2		0		1		2
	1		2		0		2
	0		2	2		3	

Codeword

Each number in this grid represents a different letter. Solve the code to create a complete crossword grid, using only English words (no proper nouns or abbreviations).

You can use the table beneath the grid to keep track of the code, and can cross off used letters along both sides of the grid.

A	■	14	■	1	■	21	■	13	■	13	■	7	■	N
B	4	18	5	8	23	12	■	10	19	12	10	15	23	O
C	■	3	■	10	■	13	■	25	■	18	■	12	■	P
D	17	10	9	20	■	13	4	10	15	4	7	3	21 G	Q
E	■	4	■	■	■	7	■	15	■	2	■	24	■	R
F	23	7	13	9	7	1	14	7	3	8	13	■	■	S
G	■	9	■	12	■	■	■	■	■	15	■	18	■	T
H	■	■	7	3	4	8	15	22 V	8	3	7	3 N	21	U
I	■	14	■	25	■	15	■	7	■	■	■	2	■	V
J	13	7	16	18	14	10	4	8	■	23	15	10	16	W
K	■	4	■	13	■	13	■	26	■	12	■	1	■	X
L	19	15	8	8	11	8	■	8	6	18	7	1	13	Y
M	■	8	■	23	■	13	■	15	■	15	■	24	■	Z

1	2	3	4	5	6	7	8	9	10	11	12	13
14	15	16	17	18	19	20	21	22	23	24	25	26

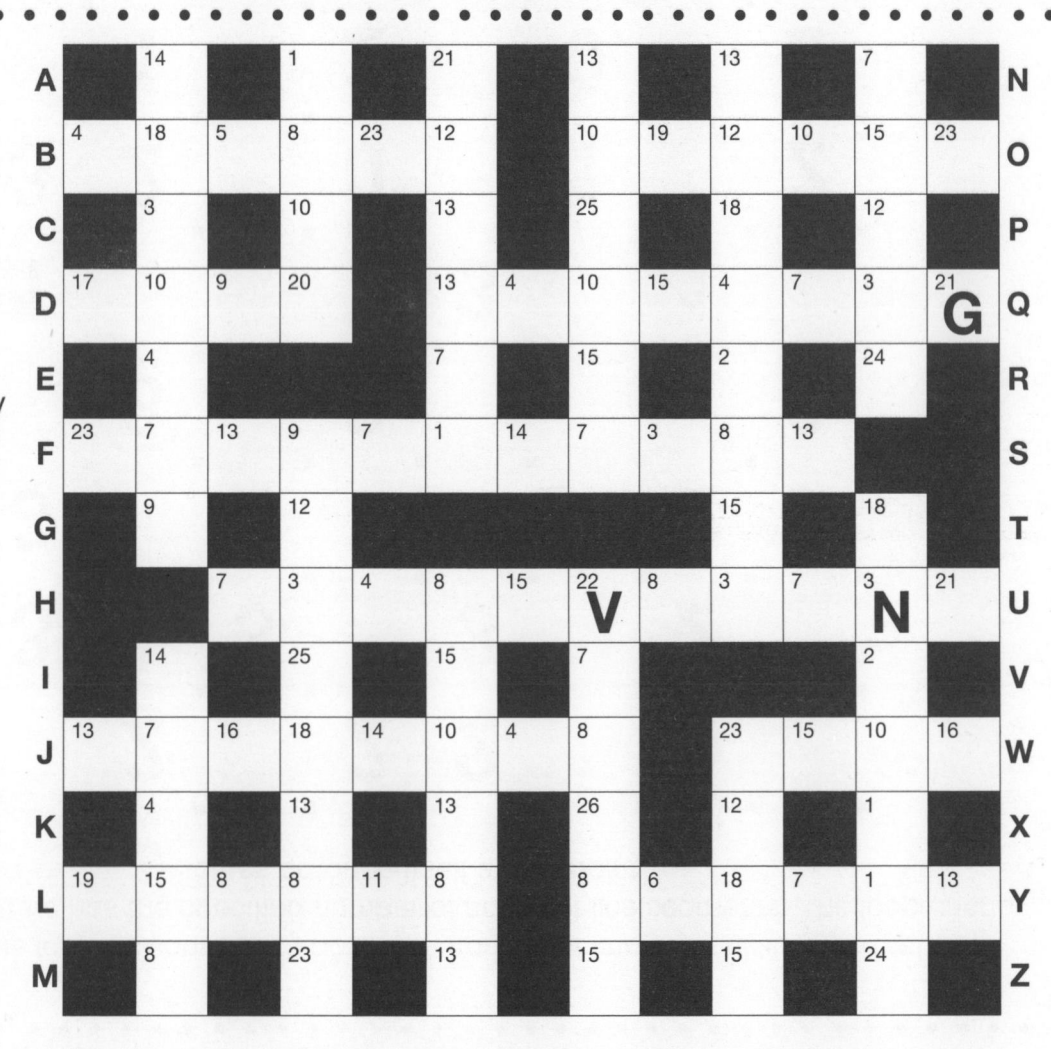

Rectangles

Draw rectangles along the grid lines so that each number ends up in a rectangle containing exactly that many cells. Each cell must be in exactly one rectangle – so rectangles cannot overlap.

			3						2
2	8				2			6	
		4		3					
				9		6		6	7
7									
		3			8				
		3			12				
2					3			4	

Kakuro

Place a number in the range 1–9 into every white cell, so that every horizontal run of white cells adds up to the number given to its left, and every vertical run of white cells adds up to the number given above it. No number can be repeated within a run.

■	■	■	37\	13\	■	15\	17\	■	■
■	■	24\17			\17			19\	16\
■	4\18				3\30				
\17				12\3			34\17		
\25						16\3			■
■	■	18\5			17\17			23\	16\
■	4\16			24\34					
\11			9\17			10\24			
\20					\15				■
■	■	\9			\16			■	■

Futoshiki

Place 1 to 8 once each into every row and column while obeying the inequality signs. Less than ('<') and greater than ('>') signs between some squares indicate that the values in these two squares must be greater than, or less than, one another, as indicated by the sign.

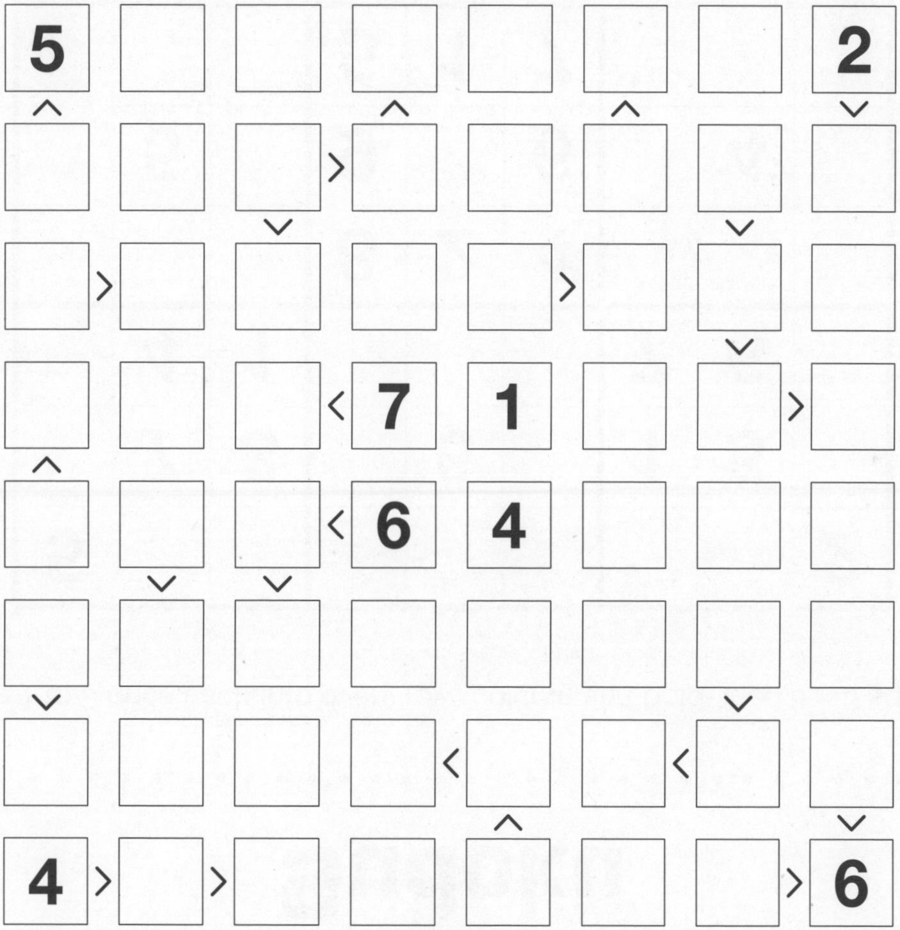

Sudoku

Place 1 to 9 once each into every row, column and bold-lined 3 × 3 square.

5								2
	7	3		6		1	5	
	4	1				7	6	
			8	2	4			
	5		9		6		4	
			5	1	7			
	2	5				8	1	
	6	4		7		3	9	
1								4

Letter Circle

Can you find the nine-letter word hidden in this Letter Circle? Form words by using the centre letter and a combination of two or more other letters from the circle. How many other words can you find?

Word Square

Can you find the 16-letter word hidden in this Word Square? Find words by moving from letter to touching letter, excluding diagonally, and without revisiting a square in a single word. How many other words can you find?

L	A	N	O
L	S	T	I
Y	N	I	T
C	O	T	U

Crossword

Across

1 Prejudices (6)
4 Extended (6)
8 Brazilian port (3)
9 Flexible (9)
11 Heroic (4)
12 Range of colours (8)
15 Medical treatment centres (9)
18 To do with the Middle Ages (8)
19 Mild, creamy cheese (4)
21 Brief, personal narratives (9)
23 Photo cards (abbr) (3)
24 Sets of ammunition (6)
25 Fantasy beast (6)

Down

1 Bleak and lifeless (6)
2 Repealed (9)
3 Ages (4)
5 Absolute ruler (8)
6 Chatter (3)
7 Imagined (6)
10 Candidate (9)
13 Keeping back (9)
14 Climbed (8)
16 Damage (6)
17 Winter, for example (6)
20 Former Russian ruler (4)
22 Euro predecessor (3)

TV Production Roles

Find each of the listed items in this wordsearch puzzle. They can be written forwards or backwards in any direction, including diagonally.

AUDIO ENGINEER
BOOM OPERATOR
CAMERA OPERATOR
CINEMATOGRAPHER
COLOURIST
COSTUME DESIGNER
CRANE OPERATOR
DIRECTOR
GAFFER
GRIP
MATTE ARTIST
PUBLICIST
RESEARCHER
RUNNER
SCREENWRITER
SET DESIGNER
STAGE MANAGER
VIDEO ENGINEER
VIDEOGRAPHER
VISION MIXER

A	R	E	N	G	I	S	E	D	E	M	U	T	S	O	C	R
T	S	E	T	D	E	S	I	G	N	E	R	R	N	D	N	M
H	D	R	H	R	E	H	P	A	R	G	O	E	D	I	V	A
E	R	L	O	P	I	O	N	P	U	B	L	I	C	I	S	T
O	S	V	S	T	A	G	E	M	A	N	A	G	E	R	R	T
R	G	R	I	P	A	R	R	G	L	N	A	G	T	R	A	E
E	D	N	E	D	D	R	G	E	R	U	E	M	E	M	T	A
T	T	P	C	T	E	N	E	O	H	O	R	F	O	E	R	R
C	S	F	R	H	I	O	N	P	T	C	F	S	G	R	R	T
E	I	R	O	T	A	R	E	P	O	A	R	E	M	A	C	I
E	R	R	R	C	F	I	W	N	G	E	M	A	R	R	T	S
I	U	A	U	D	I	O	E	N	G	I	N	E	E	R	E	T
E	O	E	O	N	O	E	N	H	E	I	P	A	N	S	E	D
T	L	G	W	S	N	E	R	M	E	E	N	C	R	I	E	V
B	O	O	M	O	P	E	R	A	T	O	R	E	A	C	C	R
I	C	N	T	O	G	S	R	G	R	O	T	C	E	R	I	D
R	E	X	I	M	N	O	I	S	I	V	S	R	S	R	F	G

Jigsaw Sudoku

Place 1 to 9 once each into every row, column and bold-lined jigsaw shape of this puzzle.

		8					3	
7				9				5
	1							
					5		6	
		5				9		
	2		6					
							2	
1				3				6
	9					5		

Going Round in Circles

Can you find a path through the maze, entering at the top and exiting at the bottom?

Number Link

Draw horizontal and vertical lines to form a set of paths, each connecting a pair of identical numbers. All numbers must be used. No more than one line can pass through any square.

				1				2	
	3					4			
					5		6		2
		7							
									8
			8				9		
			4						
	3		10				11	9	
7					5			6	
1		10							11

Calcudoku

Place 1 to 8 once each into every row and column, while obeying the clues. The value at the top left of each bold-lined region must result when the numbers in that region have the given operation (+, -, ×, ÷) applied between them. For - and ÷ operations, start with the largest number in the region and then subtract or divide by the remaining numbers.

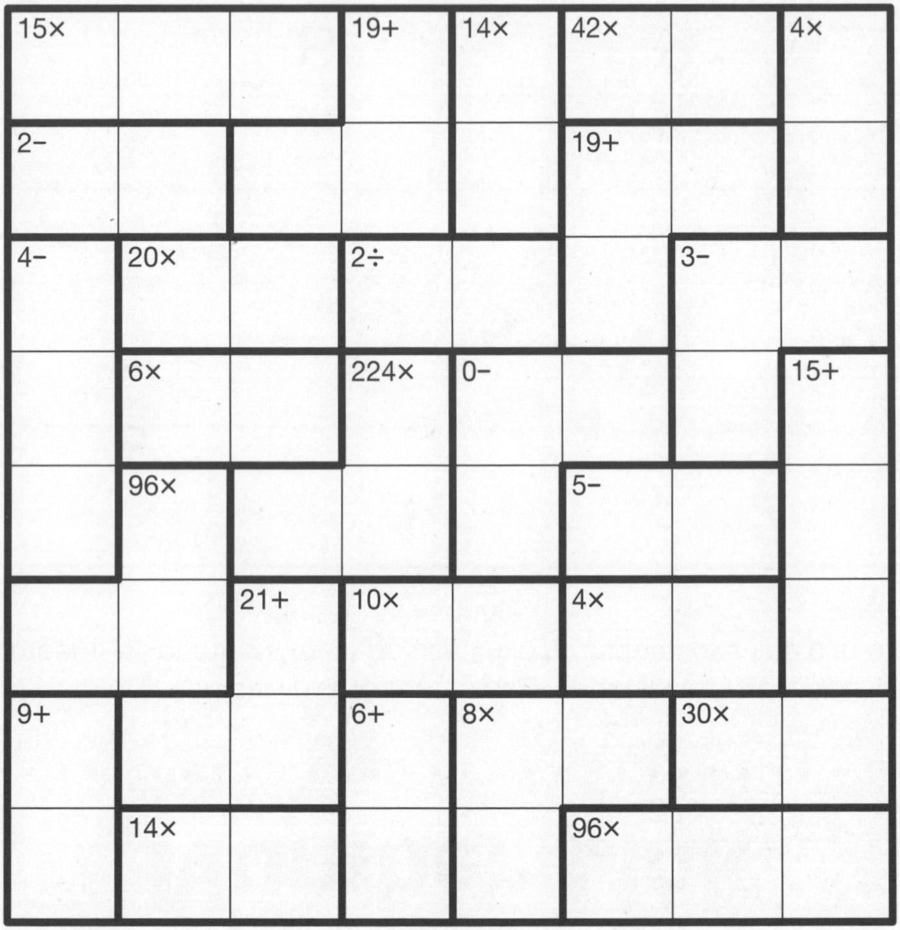

Bridges

Join circled numbers with horizontal or vertical lines so that each number has the given number of connecting lines. No more than two lines may join any pair of numbers, and lines cannot cross. The finished layout must allow you to travel from any number to any other number just by following one or more lines.

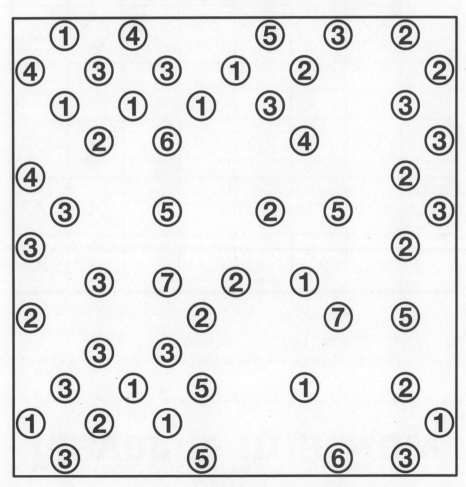

	1		4				5		3		2	
4		3		3		1		2				2
	1		1		1		3				3	
		2		6				4				3
4											2	
	3			5			2		5			3
3											2	
		3		7		2		1				
2					2				7		5	
		3		3								
	3		1		5			1			2	
1		2		1								1
	3				5				6		3	

Never 4 in a Row

Place an ‘X’ or an ‘O’ in every square, such that no continuous line of four ‘X’s or ‘O’s is made in any direction, including diagonally.

X					X		O
X	X	X				O	X
X	X		X	X	O	X	
			X				
X	O		O			X	
X	X		X	O		X	
X	X			X			X
O	O		O		X	O	X

Slitherlink

Draw a single loop by connecting dots with horizontal and vertical lines so that each numbered square has the specified number of adjacent line segments. The loop cannot cross or touch itself at any point.

	3		3	2		3	
1		1					2
	3		3		1		
3		2	2		1	1	2
2	0	2		2	3		2
		2		2		2	
1					1		3
	3		2	3		3	

Codeword

Each number in this grid represents a different letter. Solve the code to create a complete crossword grid, using only English words (no proper nouns or abbreviations).

You can use the table beneath the grid to keep track of the code, and can cross off used letters along both sides of the grid.

A	2	5	15	17	5	20	■	5	16	5	12	24	2	N
B	20	■	17	■	7	■	■	■	5	■	1	■	11	O
C	14	16	11	■	7	5	2	22	21	1	13	5	7	P
D	3	■	20	■	10	■	9	■	13	■	■	■	7	Q
E	5	26	1 I	24	■	7	21	5	11	7	18	17	20	R
F	21	■	18	■	14 O	■	1	■	24	■	1	■	5	S
G	■	■	1	12	16	5	12	24	1	14	12	■	■	T
H	26	■	5	■	5	■	23	■	26	■	11	■	25	U
I	17	12	7	5	21	20	1	5	■	18	20	5	11	V
J	2 S	■	■	■	22	■	12	■	1	■	1	■	21	W
K	5	8	22	19	11	12	23	5	2	■	6	1	23	X
L	17	■	14	■	26	■	■	■	20	■	5	■	14	Y
M	26	14	12	4	5	10	■	20	5	2	2	5	12	Z

1	2	3	4	5	6	7	8	9	10	11	12	13
14	**15**	**16**	**17**	**18**	**19**	**20**	**21**	**22**	**23**	**24**	**25**	**26**

Rectangles

Draw rectangles along the grid lines so that each number ends up in a rectangle containing exactly that many cells. Each cell must be in exactly one rectangle – so rectangles cannot overlap.

									5
3				3					
									6
					6				
		10					18		
			4						
5				4					
	9		3		3				6
2		3				4			
	4				2				

Kakuro

Place a number in the range 1–9 into every white cell, so that every horizontal run of white cells adds up to the number given to its left, and every vertical run of white cells adds up to the number given above it. No number can be repeated within a run.

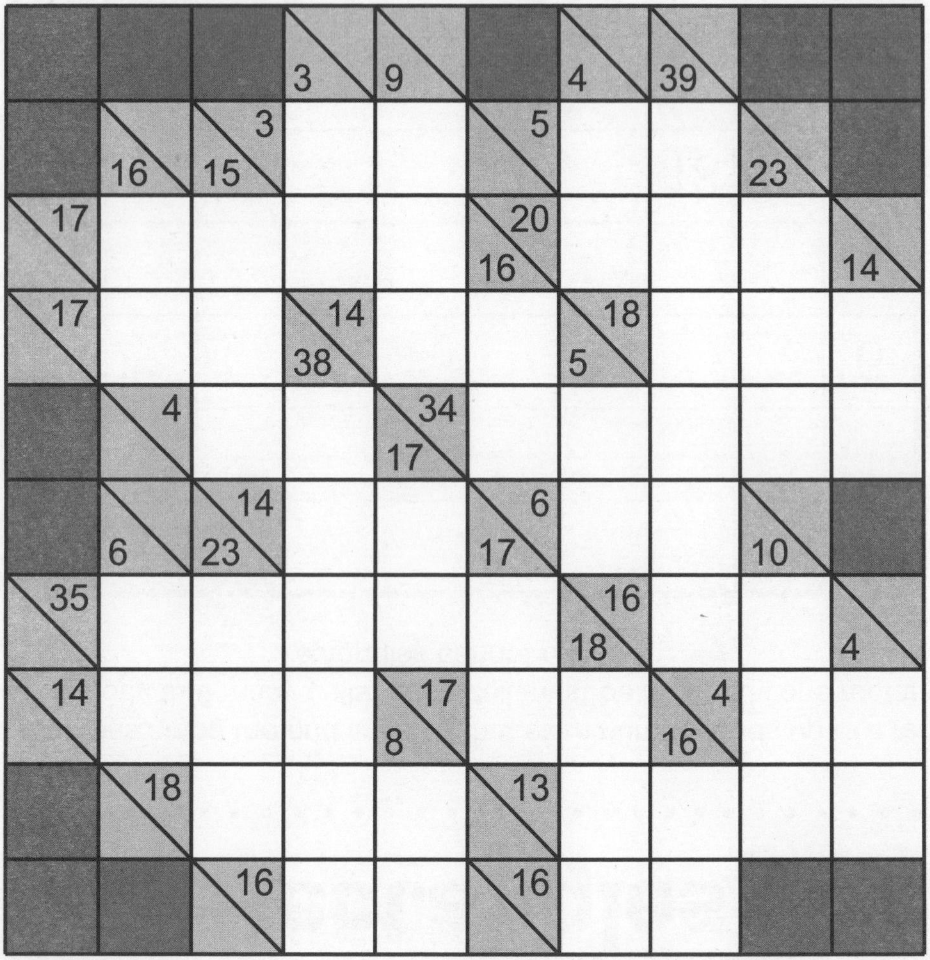

Futoshiki

Place 1 to 8 once each into every row and column while obeying the inequality signs. Less than ('<') and greater than ('>') signs between some squares indicate that the values in these two squares must be greater than, or less than, one another, as indicated by the sign.

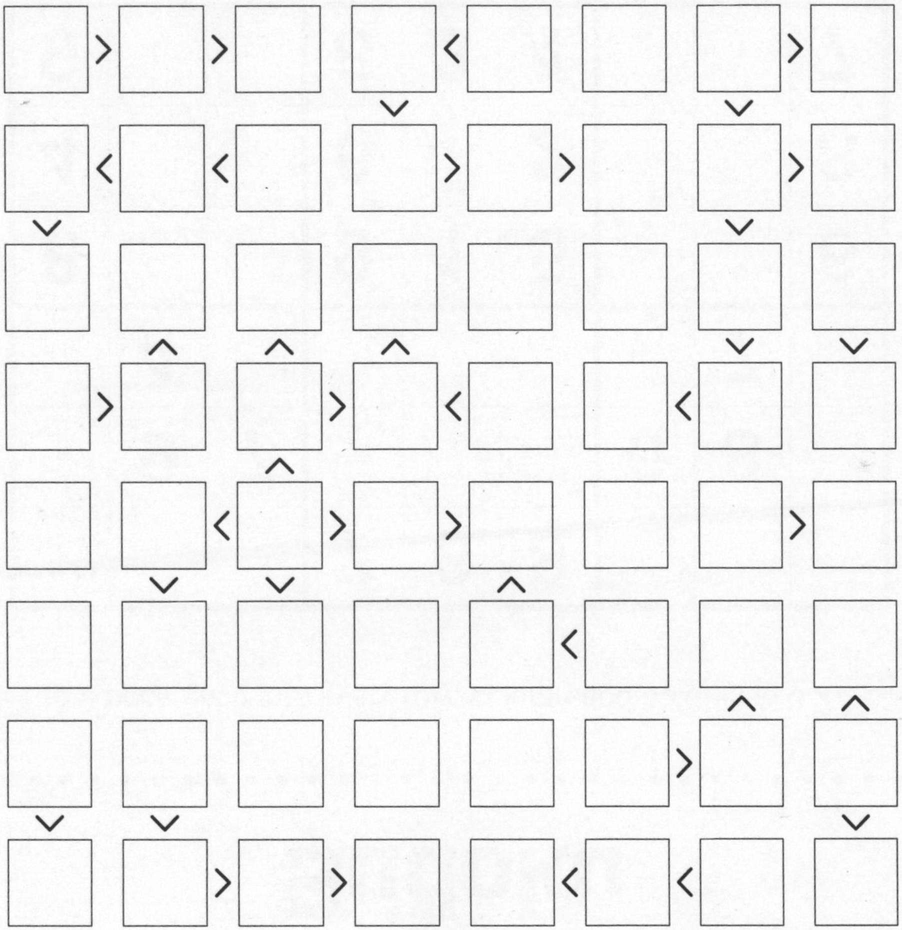

Sudoku

Place 1 to 9 once each into every row, column and bold-lined 3 × 3 square.

			7	6	8			
	9	7				6	8	
	4						7	
8			9	1	5			6
4			6		2			8
9			8	3	4			7
	3						2	
	5	6				3	1	
			2	5	3			

Letter Circle

Can you find the nine-letter word hidden in this Letter Circle? Form words by using the centre letter and a combination of two or more other letters from the circle. How many other words can you find?

C

T I

T M E

E M

O

Word Square

Can you find the 16-letter word hidden in this Word Square? Find words by moving from letter to touching letter, excluding diagonally, and without revisiting a square in a single word. How many other words can you find?

O	N	A	Y
I	C	L	L
T	O	N	V
A	S	R	E

Crossword

Across

1 Second (5)
4 Slick (6)
10 Boundless (9)
11 And so on (abbr) (3)
12 Materials (5)
13 Skilful (6)
14 Electronic instrument (11)
18 Animal-viewing expedition (6)
20 No longer a child (5)
23 Darken the skin (3)
24 Astonishingly (9)
25 Monetary fund (6)
26 Sows (5)

Down

2 Regulated (5)
3 Remove (7)
5 Optical-beam device (5)
6 Antiseptic (7)
7 'Ick!' (4)
8 Feather (5)
9 Base 16 number system (11)
15 Longed for (7)
16 Conceive (7)
17 Remains (5)
19 Not asleep (5)
21 Exhorted (5)
22 Butt (4)

Archaeological Dig

Find each of the listed items in this wordsearch puzzle. They can be written forwards or backwards in any direction, including diagonally.

- ARTEFACT
- BARROW
- BEAKER
- BOWL
- BRACTEATE
- CARTOUCHE
- CAVE ART
- CROMLECH
- CUP
- FLAKE
- FLASK
- HAND AXE
- HIEROGLYPH
- HOARD
- JAR
- LYNCHET
- MEGALITH
- MOUND
- PAPYRUS
- TUMULUS

T	C	T	D	G	H	H	H	V	E	D	M	U	L	D	L	M
S	U	L	U	M	U	T	M	O	T	B	O	B	K	E	A	G
C	T	A	D	C	I	R	E	Y	R	E	K	A	E	B	A	E
A	U	C	R	L	A	H	H	A	N	D	A	X	E	N	T	M
A	C	N	A	E	R	R	C	S	E	M	H	B	E	A	F	R
A	D	G	O	F	R	T	U	E	L	N	Y	F	B	P	U	F
S	E	I	H	I	E	R	O	G	L	Y	P	H	O	L	Y	S
M	B	E	L	A	Y	T	T	F	N	M	B	R	G	B	O	R
E	A	I	T	P	E	E	R	L	J	M	O	U	N	D	B	H
A	B	E	A	L	U	H	A	A	W	O	R	R	A	B	N	E
O	T	P	S	A	T	C	C	S	E	O	G	Y	C	N	Y	C
T	L	C	Y	T	O	N	A	K	U	V	B	C	A	D	U	E
R	E	E	R	O	X	Y	A	L	B	J	A	R	P	Y	R	E
S	A	E	O	V	X	L	O	O	S	C	A	C	G	E	C	A
O	S	A	M	L	F	M	L	A	E	X	L	A	B	U	H	A
G	T	G	A	M	L	L	U	L	T	B	M	O	L	I	M	O
P	K	N	N	Y	C	M	I	Y	O	K	M	G	L	E	T	A

Jigsaw Sudoku

Place 1 to 9 once each into every row, column and bold-lined jigsaw shape of this puzzle.

			2			4		8
			9					
9				3			5	
		8						
5		2				8		1
						1		
	9			7				3
					1			
2		7			9			

Going Round in Circles

Can you find a path through the maze, entering at the top and exiting at the bottom?

Number Link

Draw horizontal and vertical lines to form a set of paths, each connecting a pair of identical numbers. All numbers must be used. No more than one line can pass through any square.

		1				2		3	
				4		5			
	6	7							
		1				6			3
					8	9		2	9
	10							5	
			7		11			11	
4	10				8				

Calcudoku

Place 1 to 8 once each into every row and column, while obeying the clues. The value at the top left of each bold-lined region must result when the numbers in that region have the given operation (+, -, ×, ÷) applied between them. For - and ÷ operations, start with the largest number in the region and then subtract or divide by the remaining numbers.

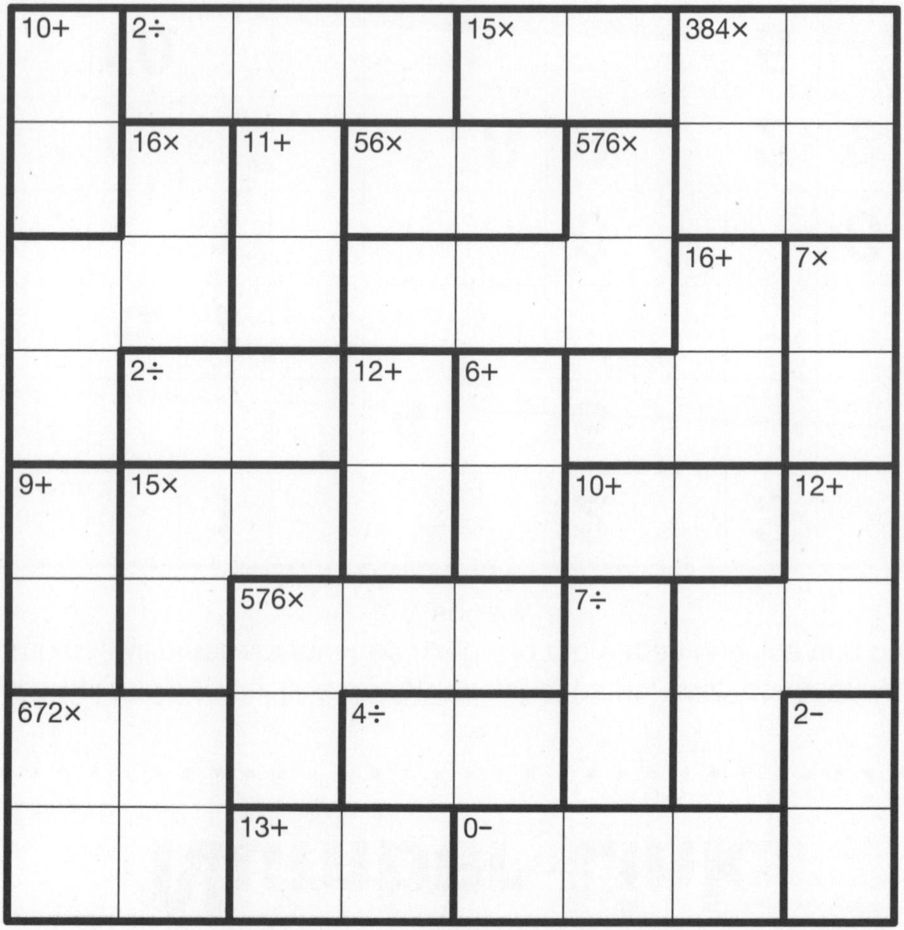

Bridges

Join circled numbers with horizontal or vertical lines so that each number has the given number of connecting lines. No more than two lines may join any pair of numbers, and lines cannot cross. The finished layout must allow you to travel from any number to any other number just by following one or more lines.

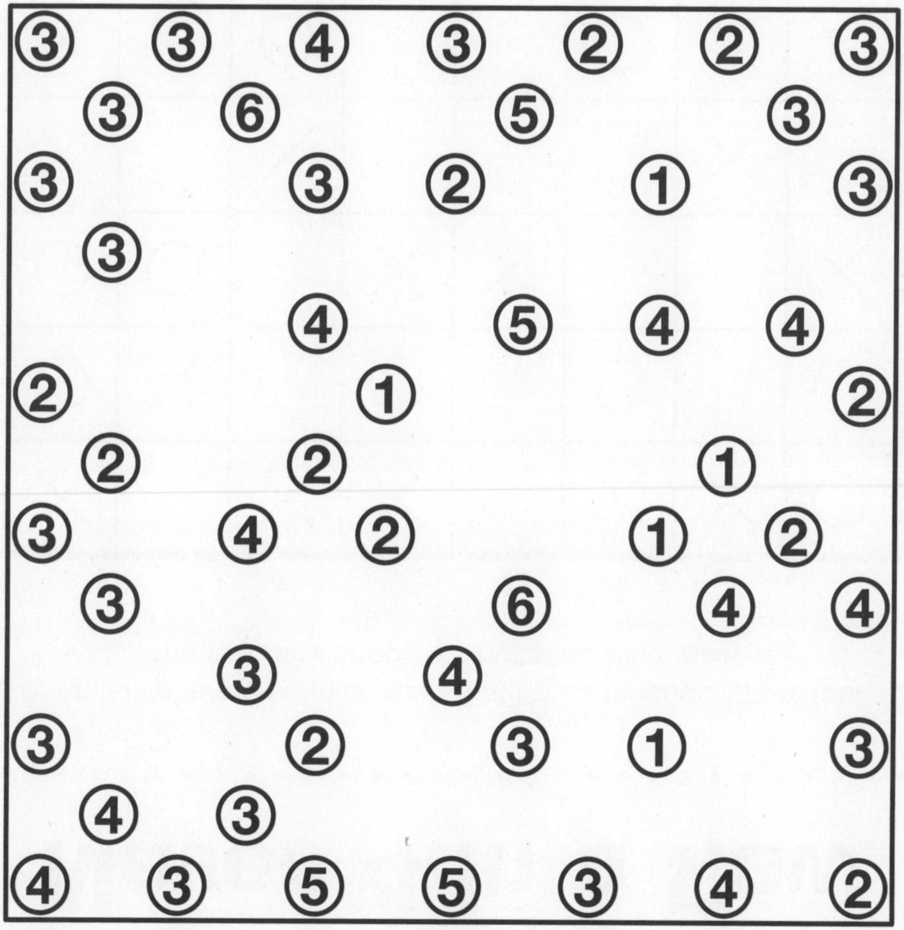

Never 4 in a Row

Place an 'X' or an 'O' in every square, such that no continuous line of four 'X's or 'O's is made in any direction, including diagonally.

X		X	X		X	X	O
O	X		O		O		O
O	O		X	X			X
X		X				X	
X		O			O	X	
O	O		O				X
X	O	X		X	X		O
X		X	X	X		X	X

Slitherlink

Draw a single loop by connecting dots with horizontal and vertical lines so that each numbered square has the specified number of adjacent line segments. The loop cannot cross or touch itself at any point.

	3		3		2		1
	1	1		0	1	2	
3		3		1		2	2
			2		1		
		3		3			
1	1		2		1		3
	3	2	1		0	1	
2		1		3		2	

Codeword

Each number in this grid represents a different letter. Solve the code to create a complete crossword grid, using only English words (no proper nouns or abbreviations).

You can use the table beneath the grid to keep track of the code, and can cross off used letters along both sides of the grid.

A	■	12	16	20	2	22	■	26	16	19	20	23	14	N
B	4	■	23	■	26	■	7	■	4	■	25	■	20	O
C	20	15	15	18	7	23	1	5	14	■	16	7	23	P
D	15	■	10	■	18	■	4	■	1	■	14	■	21	Q
E	2	18	9	18	23	■	7	1	15	20	10	9	■	R
F	26	■	■	■	10	■	18	■	■	■	17	■	■	S
G	■	14	4	1	2	10	20	9	10	6	1	21	■	T
H	■	■	20	■	■	■	2	■	23	■	■	■	16	U
I	■	24	7	18	13	15	26	■	26	16	23	15 T	14	V
J	3	■	20	■	10	■	11	■	20	■	20	■	20	W
K	20	21	21	■	14	15	16	19	25	9	10	23	24	X
L	10	■	18	■	1	■	9	■	10	■	17	■	1	Y
M	9	16	8	16	7 R	5	■	14	15	1 E	1	7	■	Z

1	2	3	4	5	6	7	8	9	10	11	12	13
14	15	16	17	18	19	20	21	22	23	24	25	26

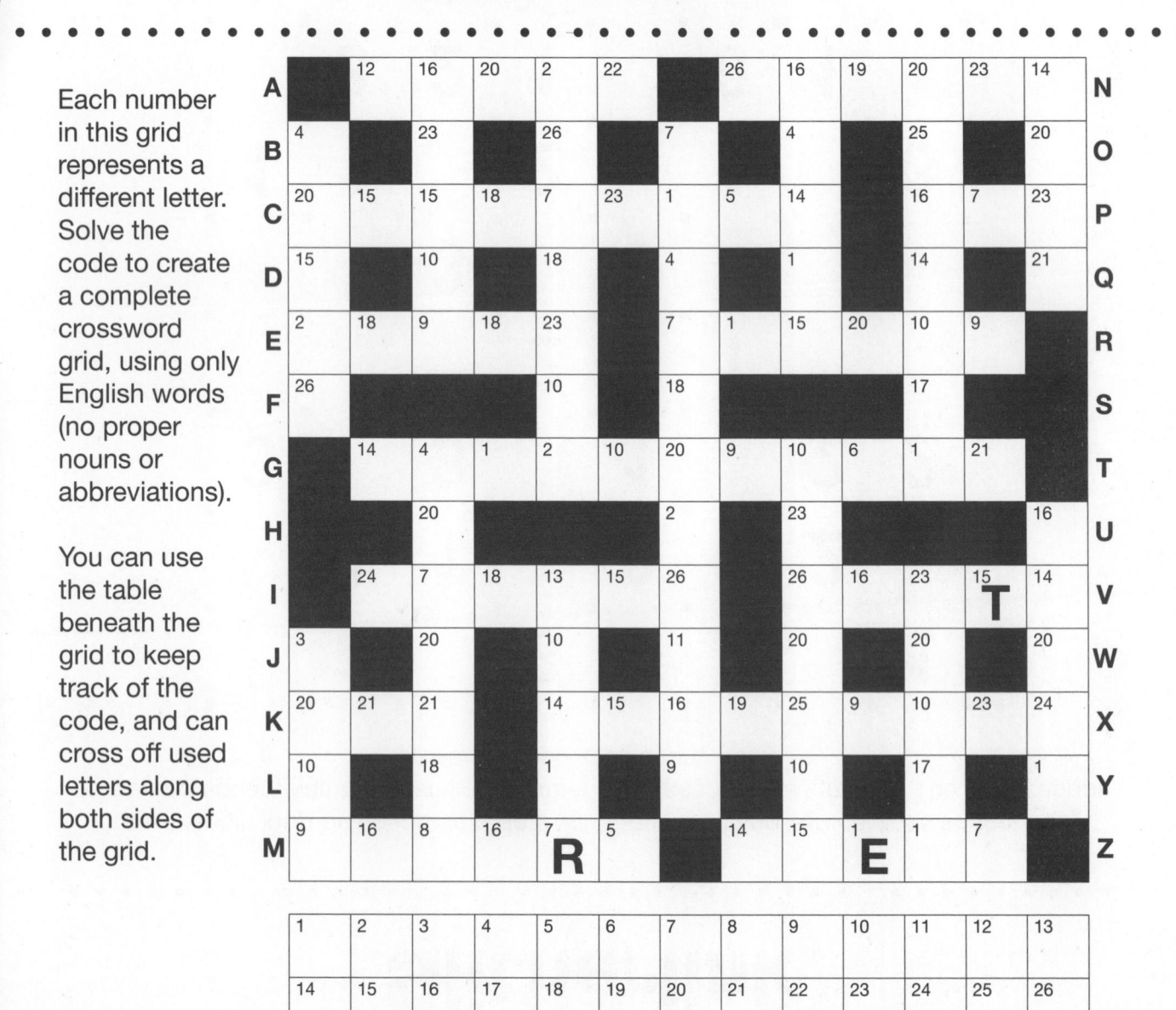

Rectangles

Draw rectangles along the grid lines so that each number ends up in a rectangle containing exactly that many cells. Each cell must be in exactly one rectangle – so rectangles cannot overlap.

4		4							
			10						
	6				10			18	
6	3				3				
	6			10					
									3
							6		
	2	2			3				4

Kakuro

Place a number in the range 1–9 into every white cell, so that every horizontal run of white cells adds up to the number given to its left, and every vertical run of white cells adds up to the number given above it. No number can be repeated within a run.

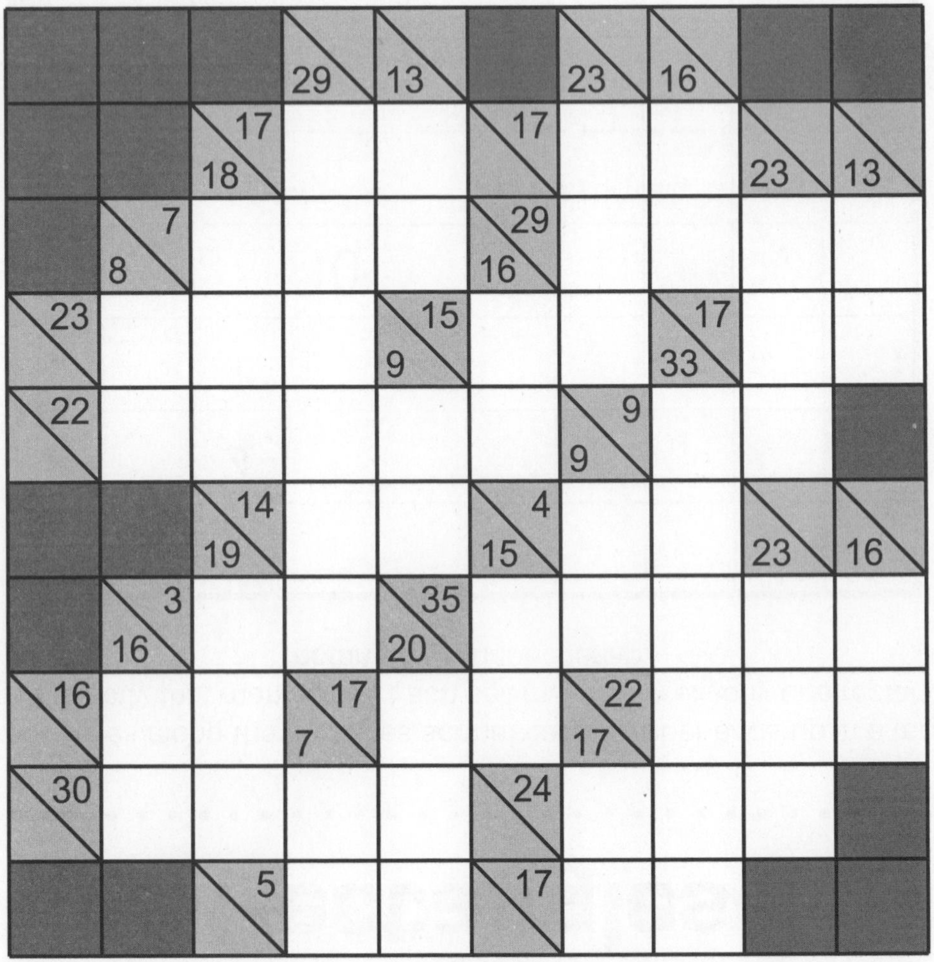

Futoshiki

Place 1 to 8 once each into every row and column while obeying the inequality signs. Less than ('<') and greater than ('>') signs between some squares indicate that the values in these two squares must be greater than, or less than, one another, as indicated by the sign.

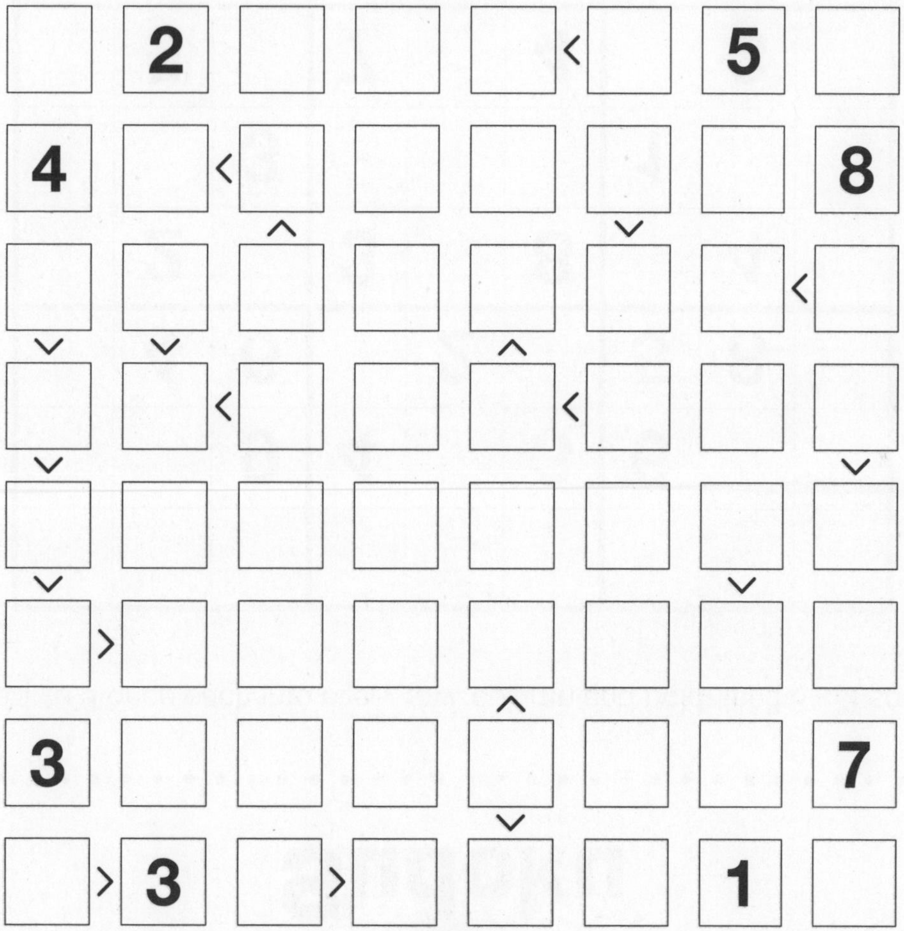

Sudoku

Place 1 to 9 once each into every row, column and bold-lined 3 × 3 square.

		9	4		3	6		
	4	6		2		5	8	
	2		3		8		4	
		3				1		
	5		7		4		3	
	6	5		9		2	1	
		4	1		6	7		

Letter Circle

Can you find the nine-letter word hidden in this Letter Circle? Form words by using the centre letter and a combination of two or more other letters from the circle. How many other words can you find?

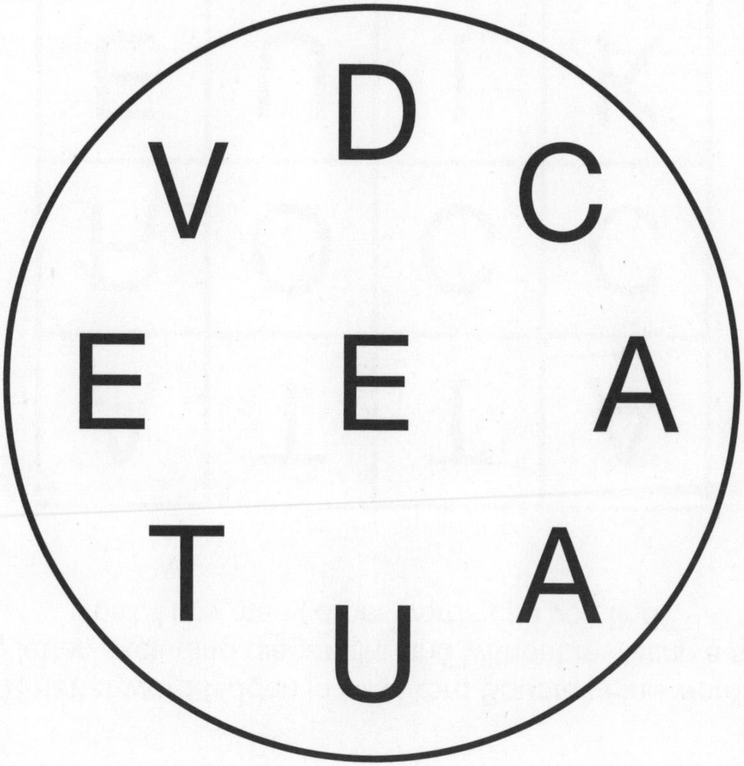

Word Square

Can you find the 16-letter word hidden in this Word Square? Find words by moving from letter to touching letter, excluding diagonally, and without revisiting a square in a single word. How many other words can you find?

A	T	T	A
R	O	C	C
E	U	I	K
T	N	N	G

Crossword

Across

1 Crush (6)
4 Unmoving (6)
9 Anxious (7)
10 Rule as monarch (5)
11 Terrifying person (4)
12 Offensive (7)
14 Discover (6)
16 Feature (6)
19 Mail deliverer (7)
21 Harsh (4)
23 Ice house (5)
24 Non-professional (7)
25 Amass (6)
26 Modified text (6)

Down

1 Cut (4)
2 Vertical (7)
3 Happy expression (5)
5 Shoves (7)
6 Clan (5)
7 Abstract ideas (8)
8 Expression (5)
13 Embracing (8)
15 Write music (7)
17 Distinguished (7)
18 Informer (5)
20 Rend (5)
21 Sentry (5)
22 Stepped (4)

It's The End

Find each of the listed items in this wordsearch puzzle. They can be written forwards or backwards in any direction, including diagonally.

- ACHIEVED
- CEASED
- CLINCHED
- CLOSED DOWN
- COMPLETED
- CONCLUDED
- CURTAINED OFF
- DEPLETED
- EMPTIED
- ENDED
- EXHAUSTED
- FINISHED
- GOT IT DONE
- LAST STAGE
- PERFECTED
- SCORED
- STOPPED
- TERMINATED
- WOUND UP
- WRAPPED UP

F	T	D	E	L	P	C	R	S	I	O	E	R	R	N	D	R
D	I	P	E	A	E	A	D	C	G	T	I	V	A	E	E	D
I	E	U	C	D	R	U	X	C	S	D	H	O	T	I	D	E
E	E	D	A	F	F	R	D	S	T	E	O	E	O	S	U	V
C	E	N	E	S	E	W	N	E	E	P	L	H	E	D	L	E
W	L	U	L	I	C	R	R	D	N	P	D	I	R	N	C	I
C	O	O	P	D	T	A	N	E	E	O	C	C	E	E	N	H
A	D	W	S	D	E	P	M	D	E	T	E	L	P	M	O	C
S	C	O	R	E	D	P	M	N	E	S	A	M	E	T	C	A
U	P	X	I	T	D	E	O	E	T	S	S	O	E	U	L	F
S	I	E	E	A	R	D	T	M	T	E	E	A	D	G	I	F
M	T	T	D	N	T	U	O	S	E	F	D	N	N	N	N	R
T	U	T	C	I	D	P	T	W	U	N	N	E	I	I	C	N
E	S	U	T	M	E	A	E	P	N	A	D	S	O	S	H	G
E	D	O	C	R	G	D	N	C	E	E	H	D	I	L	E	P
A	G	N	E	E	A	R	E	A	E	E	D	X	N	D	D	W
W	C	U	R	T	A	I	N	E	D	O	F	F	E	E	L	R

Jigsaw Sudoku

Place 1 to 9 once each into every row, column and bold-lined jigsaw shape of this puzzle.

	1			2			3	
4	8	3	9				1	
			8				5	
		2	1					9
		7				6		
8					5	3		
	3				7			
	6				8	2	9	3
	9			5			6	

Going Round in Circles

Can you find a path through the maze, entering at the top and exiting at the bottom?

Number Link

Draw horizontal and vertical lines to form a set of paths, each connecting a pair of identical numbers. All numbers must be used. No more than one line can pass through any square.

						1	2	1	
3	4			5					
			6				7		
	8				6				
				9			7		
10		8					2		
	4								
	10		5	9				11	12
3						11	12		

Calcudoku

Place 1 to 8 once each into every row and column, while obeying the clues. The value at the top left of each bold-lined region must result when the numbers in that region have the given operation (+, -, ×, ÷) applied between them. For - and ÷ operations, start with the largest number in the region and then subtract or divide by the remaining numbers.

16+	12×		17+		160×		
	20×				9+		14+
	2−	48×		4÷			
		15×	2÷	5−	5−		
21+						19+	
		6×		10×			18+
	3+		450×		5−		
112×					3−		

Bridges

Join circled numbers with horizontal or vertical lines so that each number has the given number of connecting lines. No more than two lines may join any pair of numbers, and lines cannot cross. The finished layout must allow you to travel from any number to any other number just by following one or more lines.

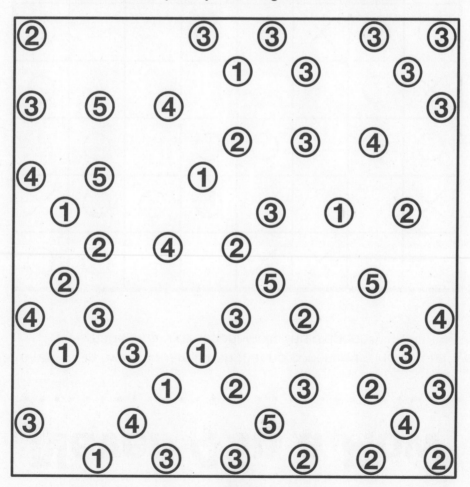

2					3		3			3		3
						1		3			3	
3		5		4								3
						2		3		4		
4		5			1							
	1						3		1		2	
		2		4		2						
	2						5			5		
4		3				3		2				4
	1		3		1						3	
				1		2		3		2		3
3			4				5				4	
		1		3		3		2		2		2

Never 4 in a Row

Place an 'X' or an 'O' in every square, such that no continuous line of four 'X's or 'O's is made in any direction, including diagonally.

O	O			X	X		
X	O	O	O				X
	O		O	O		O	O
O						O	X
O			O	O	X	O	O
O							X
	O	O		X	X	O	
O	O	X		O	O	X	

Slitherlink

Draw a single loop by connecting dots with horizontal and vertical lines so that each numbered square has the specified number of adjacent line segments. The loop cannot cross or touch itself at any point.

				2		3	
1		2		1		3	2
	3	3	1				
	1	2		2	3		1
3		3	1		1	3	
				3	2	2	
2	0		2		2		2
	1		3				

Codeword

Each number in this grid represents a different letter. Solve the code to create a complete crossword grid, using only English words (no proper nouns or abbreviations).

You can use the table beneath the grid to keep track of the code, and can cross off used letters along both sides of the grid.

A	■	20	3	3	24	15	5	1	■	15	26	3	5	**N**
B	20	■	9	■	7	■	8	■	■	20	■	23	■	**O**
C	15	21	13	24 I	15	■	6	26	12	20	4 Q	9	5	**P**
D	5	■	15	■	10	■	5	■	5	■	■	7	■	**Q**
E	26	13	7	1	■	22	12	20	8	24	1	5	1	**R**
F	13	■	24	■	1	■	1	■	26	■	26	■	■	**S**
G	■	7	20	20	7	10	■	19	12	24	23	23	■	**T**
H	■	■	13	■	26	■	1	■	25	■	18	■	26	**U**
I	10	5	1	24	7	26 A	7	5	■	11	26	12	1	**V**
J	■	2	■	■	9	■	20	■	20	■	7	■	10	**W**
K	8	24	1	12	5	26	19	■	8	26	24	16	5	**X**
L	■	23	■	9	■	■	14	■	24	■	20	■	1	**Y**
M	6	5	5	13	■	17	5	7	7	24	13	14	■	**Z**

1	2	3	4	5	6	7	8	9	10	11	12	13
14	15	16	17	18	19	20	21	22	23	24	25	26

Rectangles

Draw rectangles along the grid lines so that each number ends up in a rectangle containing exactly that many cells. Each cell must be in exactly one rectangle – so rectangles cannot overlap.

3					4				
	8					2			
						4			9
		4							
	8		3	6		6		12	
								6	
7				3					
	6			6					
								3	

Kakuro

Place a number in the range 1–9 into every white cell, so that every horizontal run of white cells adds up to the number given to its left, and every vertical run of white cells adds up to the number given above it. No number can be repeated within a run.

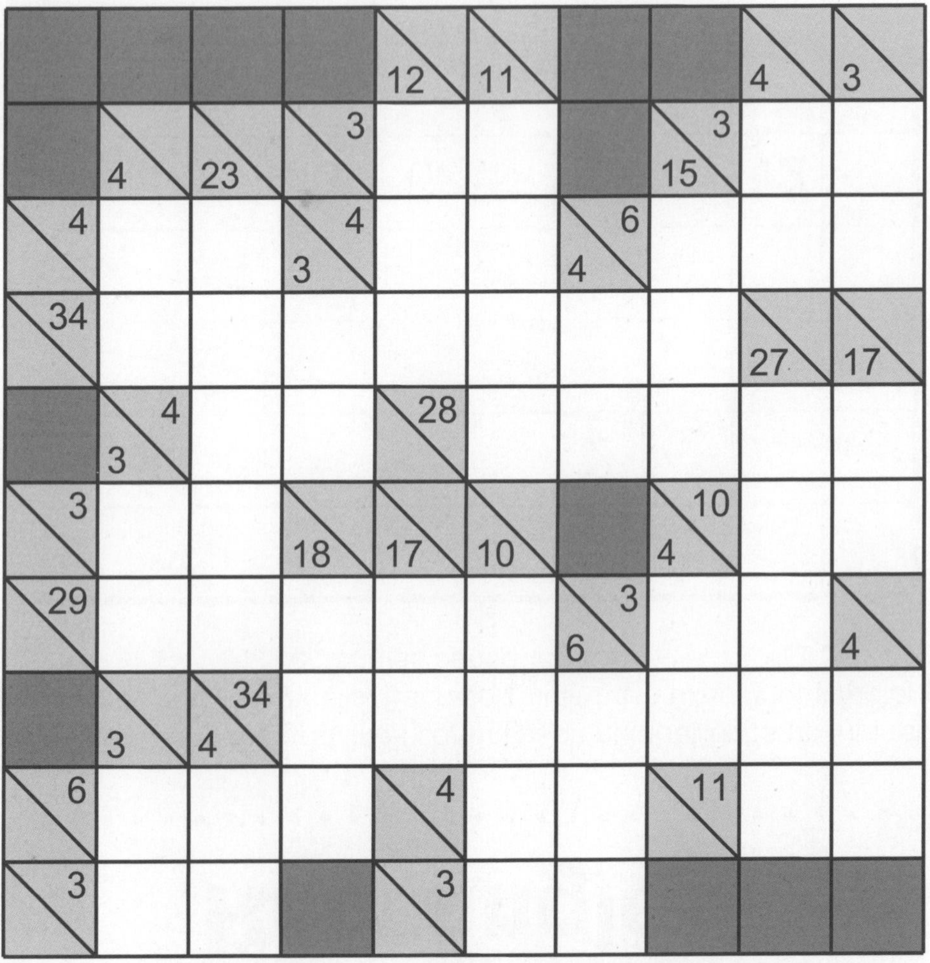

Futoshiki

Place 1 to 8 once each into every row and column while obeying the inequality signs. Less than ('<') and greater than ('>') signs between some squares indicate that the values in these two squares must be greater than, or less than, one another, as indicated by the sign.

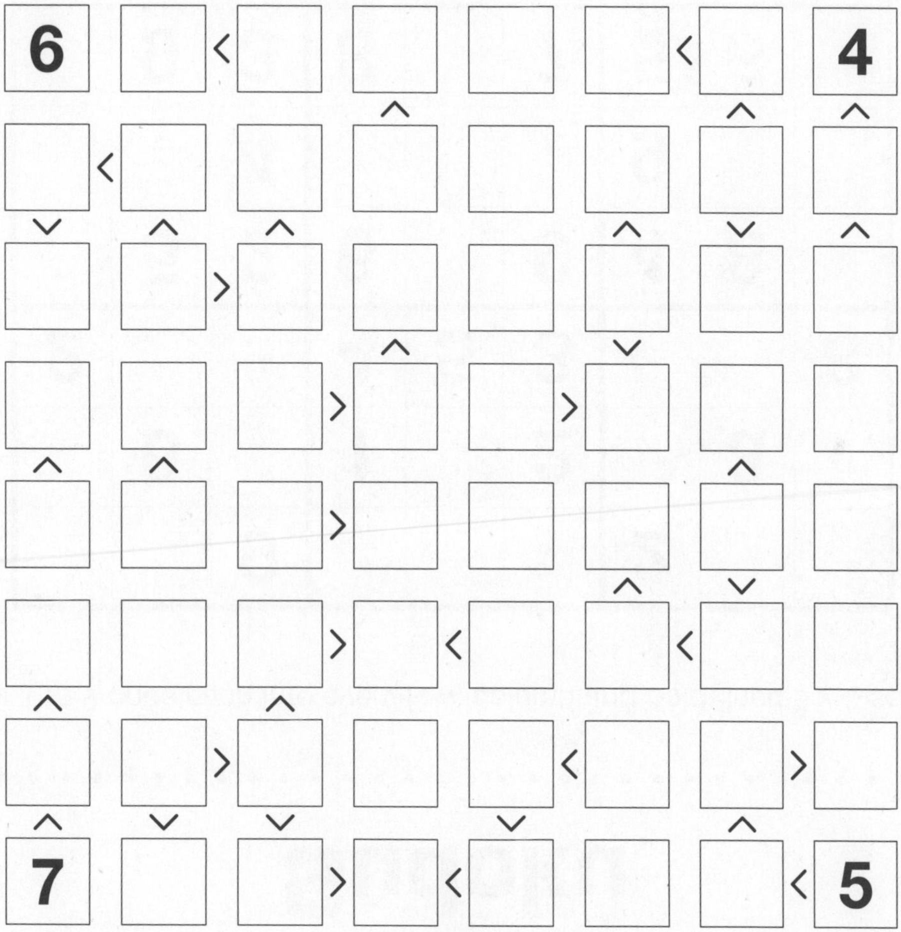

Sudoku

Place 1 to 9 once each into every row, column and bold-lined 3 × 3 square.

		9				2		
	6		1		2		3	
2			4	5	3			8
	5	2	6		9	4	8	
		4				9		
	9	3	8		7	5	6	
5			9	7	4			6
	7		2		1		5	
		1				8		

Letter Circle

Can you find the nine-letter word hidden in this Letter Circle? Form words by using the centre letter and a combination of two or more other letters from the circle. How many other words can you find?

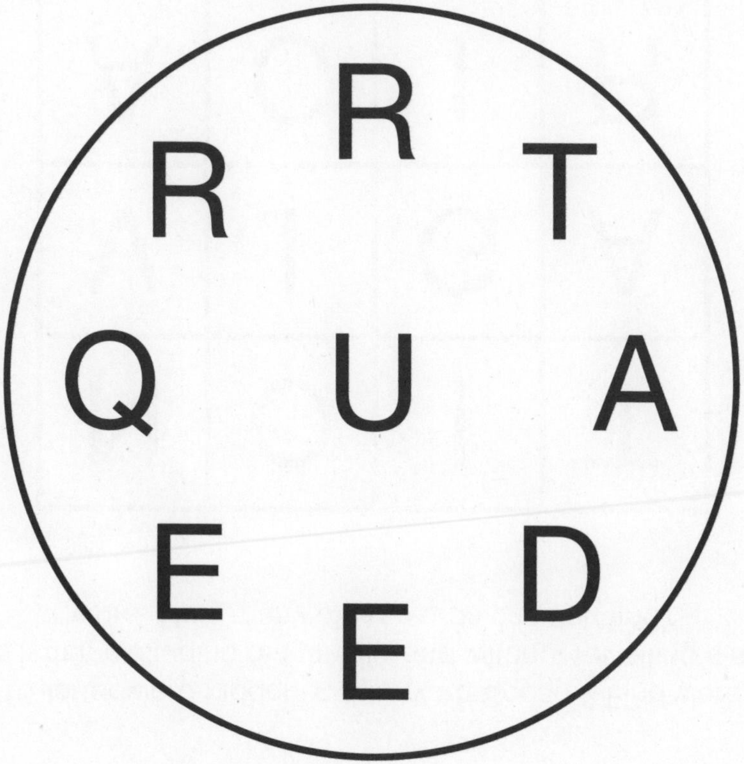

Word Square

Can you find the 16-letter word hidden in this Word Square? Find words by moving from letter to touching letter, excluding diagonally, and without revisiting a square in a single word. How many other words can you find?

N	O	I	T
V	I	G	A
A	C	I	R
N	M	U	C

Crossword

Across

1 Potato snack (6)
4 Cling (6)
9 Endorsing (9)
10 Duo (3)
11 And not (3)
12 Ill (9)
13 Used up (5)
15 Small, poisonous snake (5)
20 Infringement (9)
22 Propellant gas (inits) (3)
23 Former pope (3)
24 Practical (9)
25 Fairly (6)
26 Rarely encountered (6)

Down

1 Cover (6)
2 Become subject to (5)
3 Flightless seabird (7)
5 Tenet (5)
6 Give a right to (7)
7 A name formed from a name (6)
8 Strength (5)
14 Suggest (7)
16 Driving (7)
17 Develop over time (6)
18 Essential (5)
19 Frozen water drops (6)
21 Fill with horror (5)
22 Provide food (5)

Rivers of the World

Find each of the listed items in this wordsearch puzzle. They can be written forwards or backwards in any direction, including diagonally.

AMAZON
BARROW
CHURCHILL
INDUS
ISIS
JORDAN
LIMPOPO
LITTLE BIGHORN
MOSELLE
NIGER
NILE
ORINOCO
SEVERN
TAY
THAMES
TWEED
TYNE
VOLTA
YANGTZE
YUKON

L	E	R	O	R	O	T	T	O	L	H	K	Y	P	T	V	O
Z	H	N	Z	O	P	O	P	M	I	L	L	T	L	H	T	E
Y	U	R	L	S	M	S	U	D	N	I	D	A	Y	U	A	R
Y	P	L	N	C	I	L	M	E	Z	T	G	N	A	Y	E	Y
O	O	W	R	S	L	I	A	O	Y	T	N	O	R	A	G	O
T	I	A	I	Y	V	T	J	O	S	L	O	I	P	B	B	G
R	A	R	S	B	V	S	O	U	D	E	E	W	T	A	Y	S
T	P	M	E	A	A	O	M	C	Z	B	L	B	Y	H	Y	O
O	P	P	A	C	H	U	R	C	H	I	L	L	S	N	Z	G
R	N	A	A	Z	E	C	B	I	L	G	H	A	E	S	I	A
V	O	H	I	V	O	L	T	A	N	H	L	T	M	S	I	O
M	Z	C	W	G	O	N	A	D	R	O	J	O	A	I	N	L
H	A	N	L	C	O	N	I	G	E	R	C	P	H	O	D	N
Y	C	O	A	K	O	G	S	L	V	N	O	O	T	I	Y	U
T	P	D	U	G	U	A	L	B	E	I	Y	W	L	S	N	I
U	I	Y	O	G	A	S	G	O	S	M	O	T	A	Z	P	U
P	A	N	L	L	E	I	D	A	Y	S	I	L	B	T	S	P

Jigsaw Sudoku

Place 1 to 9 once each into every row, column and bold-lined jigsaw shape of this puzzle.

							9	3
							8	
9					3			7
	3	2		1			7	
			3		8			
	8			9		3	1	
5			8					1
	6							
7	1							

Going Round in Circles

Can you find a path through the maze, entering at the top and exiting at the bottom?

Number Link

Draw horizontal and vertical lines to form a set of paths, each connecting a pair of identical numbers. All numbers must be used. No more than one line can pass through any square.

						1		2	3
	4								
1	5		2						6
				3				4	
		7				6		8	
		9		10		9			
		5				11			
	7			10				8	
						11			

Calcudoku

Place 1 to 8 once each into every row and column, while obeying the clues. The value at the top left of each bold-lined region must result when the numbers in that region have the given operation (+, -, ×, ÷) applied between them. For - and ÷ operations, start with the largest number in the region and then subtract or divide by the remaining numbers.

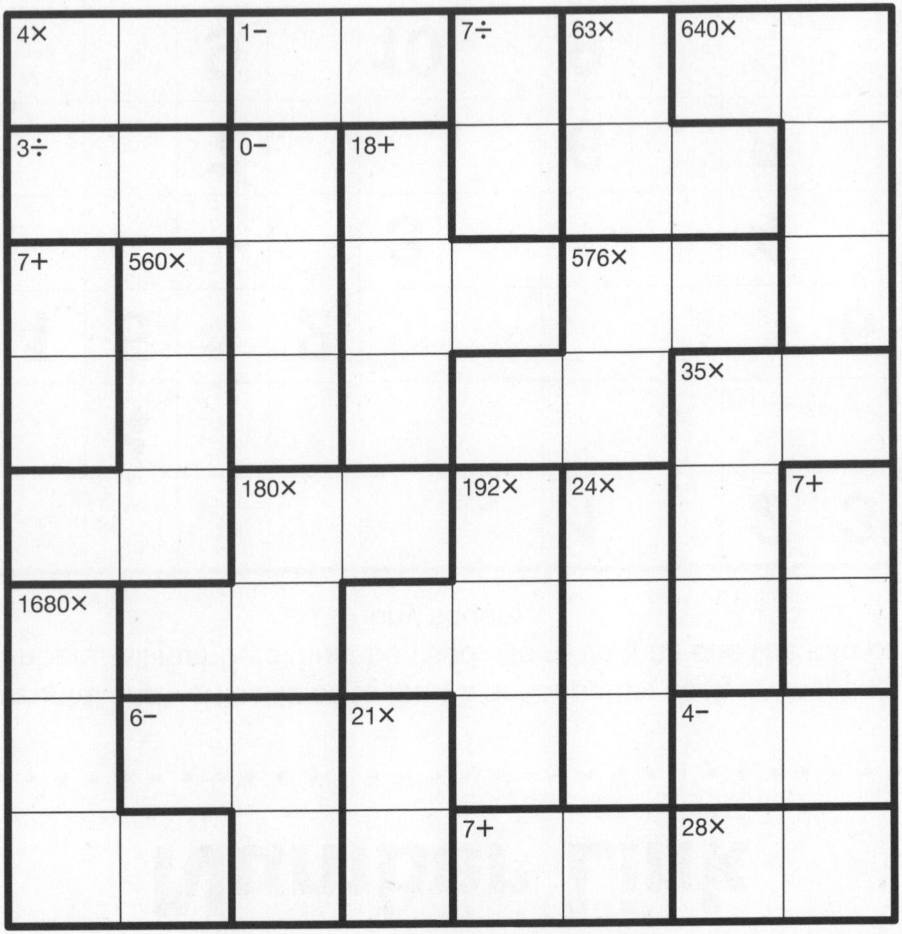

Bridges

Join circled numbers with horizontal or vertical lines so that each number has the given number of connecting lines. No more than two lines may join any pair of numbers, and lines cannot cross. The finished layout must allow you to travel from any number to any other number just by following one or more lines.

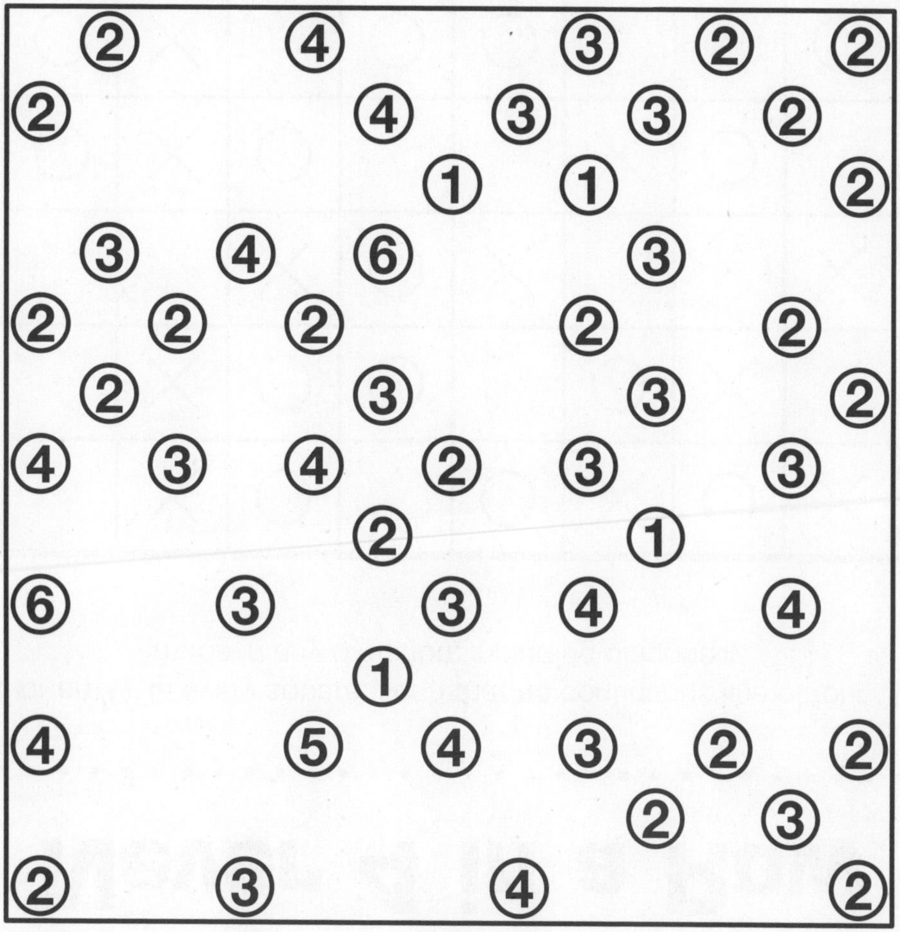

Never 4 in a Row

Place an 'X' or an 'O' in every square, such that no continuous line of four 'X's or 'O's is made in any direction, including diagonally.

	X	O		O	X	O	X
	X	O	O		O	X	
		X	O	X			X
O	X	O			X	O	
O	X		O	O			O
O	O	O			X		O
	O		X	X			O
	O		X		O	O	

Slitherlink

Draw a single loop by connecting dots with horizontal and vertical lines so that each numbered square has the specified number of adjacent line segments. The loop cannot cross or touch itself at any point.

	1				3		0
	1		1	2		2	
0		2		3		1	
2		2			1		2
2		3			0		3
	2		2		2		1
	2		2	3		2	
3		1				1	

Codeword

Each number in this grid represents a different letter. Solve the code to create a complete crossword grid, using only English words (no proper nouns or abbreviations).

You can use the table beneath the grid to keep track of the code, and can cross off used letters along both sides of the grid.

A	■	20	19	24	7	25 L	18	26	■	4	1 B	18	12 T	N
B	13	■	12	■	8	■	5	■	4	■	4	■	4	O
C	18	5	15	22	1	22	12	■	9	4	6	4	25	P
D	12	■	18	■	4	■	18	■	21	■	24	■	3	Q
E	4	2	8	19	6	■	6	18	7	8	4	25	■	R
F	16	■	■	■	22	■	12	■	4	■	6	■	8	S
G	4	1	25	4	11	18	■	24	22	25	4	12	18	T
H	17	■	18	■	4	■	26	■	6	■	■	■	10	U
I	■	1	4	12	12	25	18	■	12	18	2	18	18	V
J	14	■	23	■	22	■	8	■	4	■	8	■	6	W
K	22	13	25	19	19	■	10	18	6	24	22	6	13	X
L	10	■	18	■	6	■	18	■	9	■	6	■	18	Y
M	18	4	12	26	■	4	26	2	18	9	12	26	■	Z

1	2	3	4	5	6	7	8	9	10	11	12	13
14	15	16	17	18	19	20	21	22	23	24	25	26

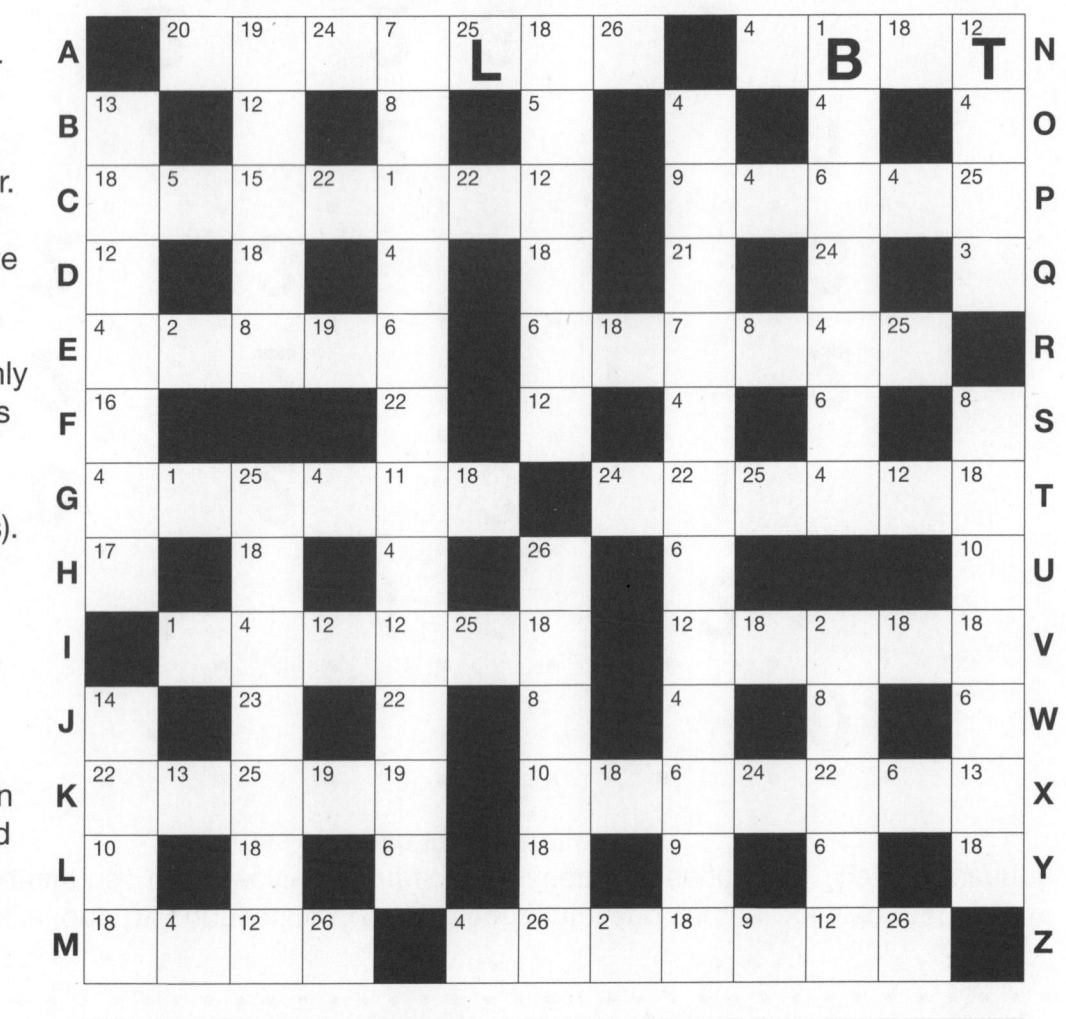

Rectangles

Draw rectangles along the grid lines so that each number ends up in a rectangle containing exactly that many cells. Each cell must be in exactly one rectangle – so rectangles cannot overlap.

	12				2				2
					3	6			
	4							8	
4	3								
			4	5					
						20			
		8		3					
						4			
2		8							2

Kakuro

Place a number in the range 1–9 into every white cell, so that every horizontal run of white cells adds up to the number given to its left, and every vertical run of white cells adds up to the number given above it. No number can be repeated within a run.

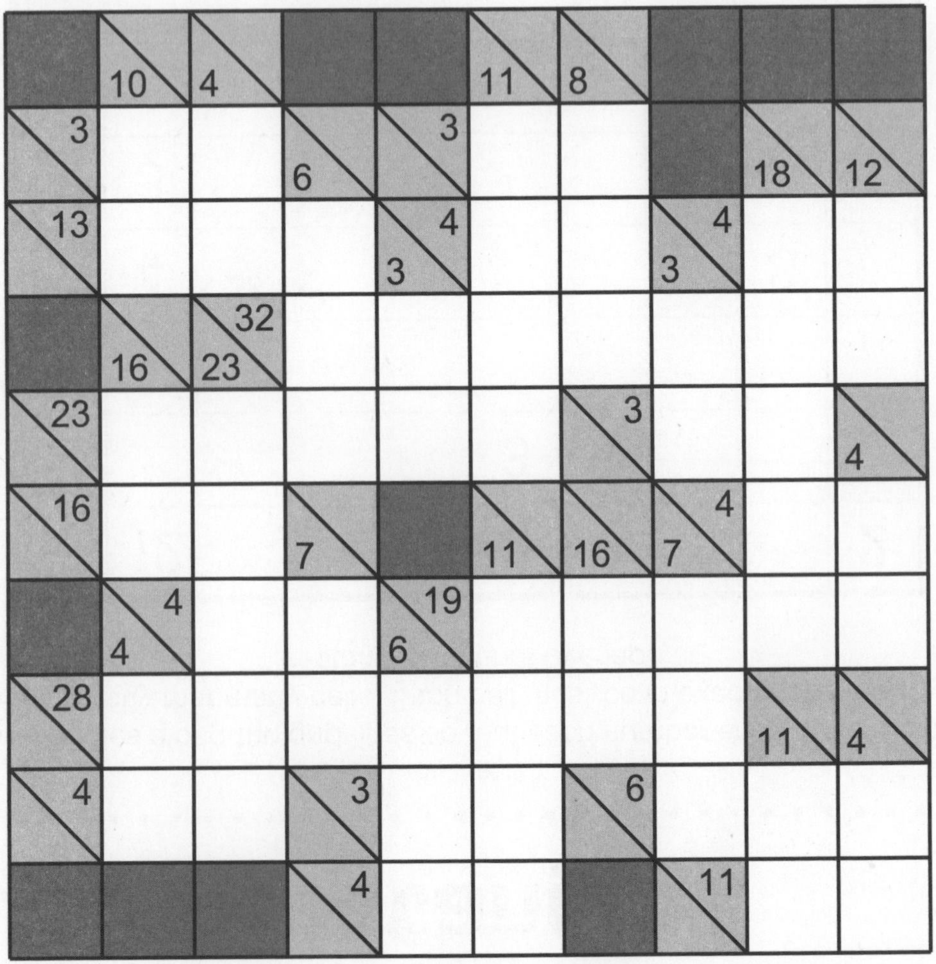

Futoshiki

Place 1 to 8 once each into every row and column while obeying the inequality signs. Less than ('<') and greater than ('>') signs between some squares indicate that the values in these two squares must be greater than, or less than, one another, as indicated by the sign.

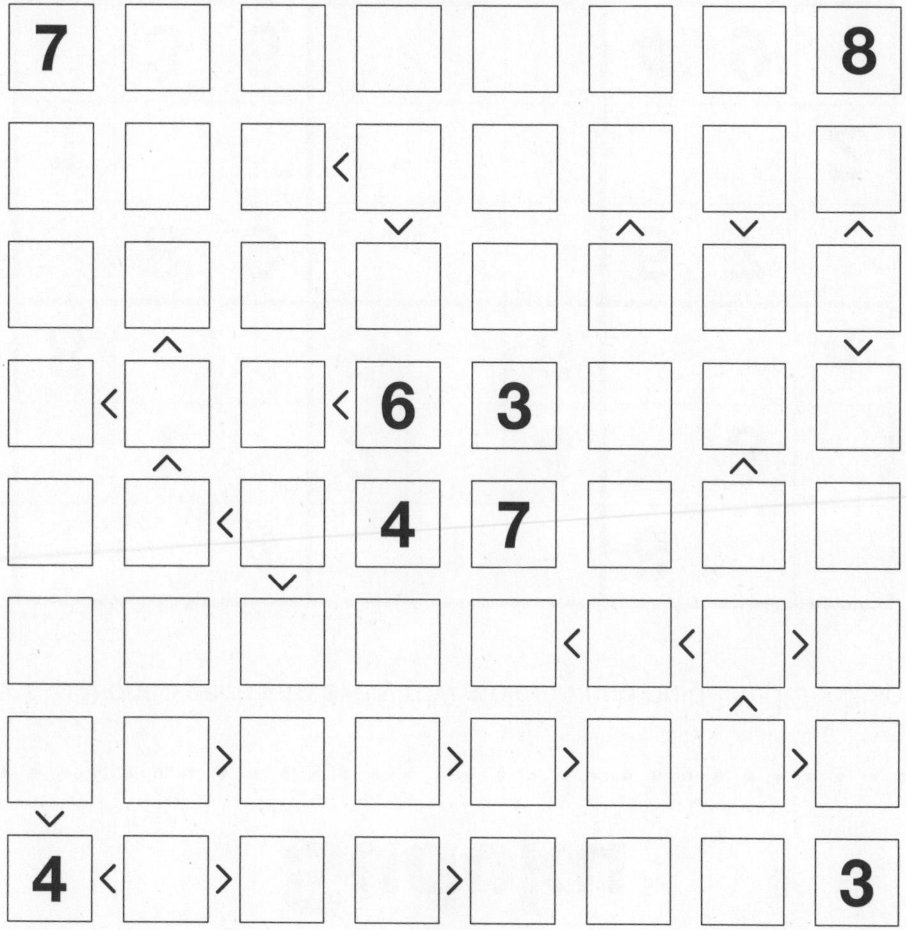

Sudoku

Place 1 to 9 once each into every row, column and bold-lined 3 × 3 square.

		4		1		8		
	1		2		4		3	
8			5		6			4
	8	9				5	7	
1								2
	3	6				4	9	
5			8		7			9
	9		6		2		8	
		8		4		2		

Letter Circle

Can you find the nine-letter word hidden in this Letter Circle? Form words by using the centre letter and a combination of two or more other letters from the circle. How many other words can you find?

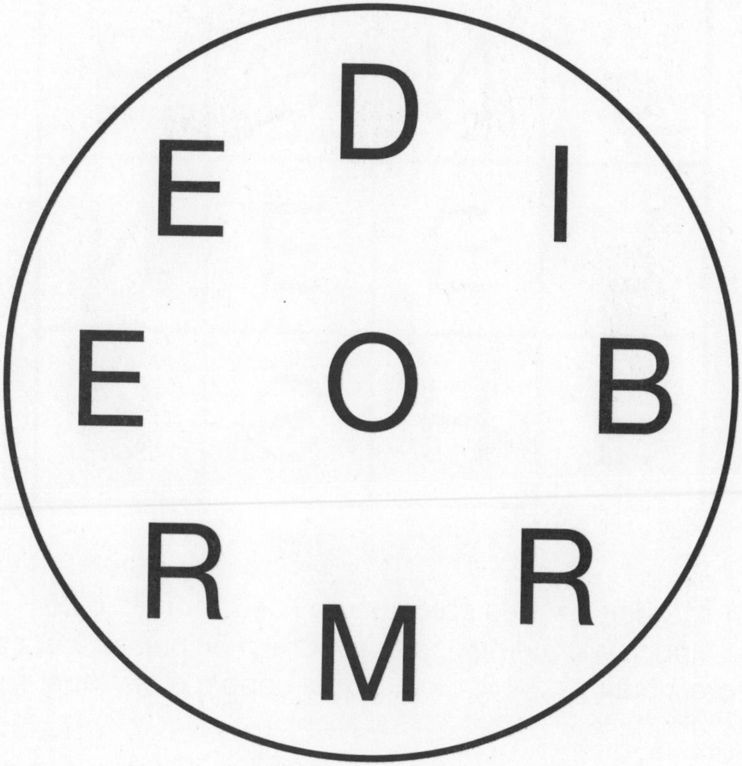

Word Square

Can you find the 16-letter word hidden in this Word Square? Find words by moving from letter to touching letter, excluding diagonally, and without revisiting a square in a single word. How many other words can you find?

S	S	H	E
N	E	E	R
E	S	N	P
V	I	A	P

Crossword

Across

7 Rich, moist cake (6)
8 Probable (6)
9 Astound (4)
10 Ran (8)
11 Formulation (11)
14 Divisor (11)
18 Unexplained happenings (8)
19 Conceal (4)
20 Display surface (6)
21 Death (6)

Down

1 Affairs (7)
2 Incline (4)
3 Gossip (6)
4 Well spoken (6)
5 US state (8)
6 Rest in bed (5)
12 The Queen can confer these honours on subjects who please her (8)
13 Noisiest (7)
15 Hooked up to the Internet (6)
16 Internal (6)
17 About (5)
19 Sews a cloth edge (4)

Types of Cloud

Find each of the listed items in this wordsearch puzzle. They can be written forwards or backwards in any direction, including diagonally.

ALTOCUMULUS
ALTOSTRATUS
CASTELLANUS
CIRROCUMULUS
CIRROSTRATUS
CIRRUS
CUMULOGENITUS
CUMULONIMBUS
FIBRATUS
INCUS
INTORTUS
LACUNOSUS
NIMBOSTRATUS
OPACUS
PILEUS
STRATIFORMIS
STRATOCUMULUS
UNCINUS
UNDULATUS
VELUM

V	F	M	R	T	L	S	A	S	U	B	M	S	L	I	O	A
S	T	R	S	O	U	S	U	C	A	P	O	I	T	T	O	U
A	L	B	S	O	C	T	T	S	L	M	T	M	S	N	I	S
A	U	C	U	I	A	L	S	S	U	T	A	R	B	I	F	F
C	O	S	S	L	S	M	U	U	S	L	S	O	E	M	I	L
I	U	R	U	R	T	N	B	L	O	U	C	F	C	B	V	C
R	S	D	T	L	E	L	M	M	T	A	I	I	A	O	C	I
R	N	O	I	I	L	N	I	U	L	U	R	T	M	S	S	T
U	L	V	N	L	L	S	N	T	S	R	R	A	M	T	I	S
S	S	C	E	T	A	S	O	O	O	S	O	R	C	R	R	I
T	U	T	G	L	N	C	L	C	M	C	S	T	S	A	N	U
S	N	T	O	S	U	S	U	T	A	R	T	S	O	T	L	A
T	I	U	L	M	S	M	M	N	S	L	R	S	O	U	G	O
B	C	S	U	L	U	M	U	C	O	T	A	R	T	S	S	S
G	N	L	M	L	N	S	C	S	O	S	T	T	S	N	S	U
R	U	S	U	E	L	I	P	S	F	U	U	T	O	L	U	T
S	S	S	C	M	O	S	I	M	S	A	S	S	L	U	B	S

Jigsaw Sudoku

Place 1 to 9 once each into every row, column and bold-lined jigsaw shape of this puzzle.

4	1				9			
	8					5		9
	2							
						1		
			1		8			
		4						
							9	
3		7					1	
			3				5	8

Going Round in Circles

Can you find a path through the maze, entering at the top and exiting at the bottom?

Number Link

Draw horizontal and vertical lines to form a set of paths, each connecting a pair of identical numbers. All numbers must be used. No more than one line can pass through any square.

1									
						2	3		1
				4					5
		6			7				
			5						
					8			3	
2			9					4	
	6		8					7	
						9			

Calcudoku

Place 1 to 8 once each into every row and column, while obeying the clues. The value at the top left of each bold-lined region must result when the numbers in that region have the given operation (+, -, ×, ÷) applied between them. For - and ÷ operations, start with the largest number in the region and then subtract or divide by the remaining numbers.

32×		3−	2−	192×	70×		
	0−					10+	
		2÷		6×			16×
18+		48×		8+		11+	
2−		7+		3×			
	5×	6−		4÷		15+	
0−		15+		28×	10×		210×

Bridges

Join circled numbers with horizontal or vertical lines so that each number has the given number of connecting lines. No more than two lines may join any pair of numbers, and lines cannot cross. The finished layout must allow you to travel from any number to any other number just by following one or more lines.

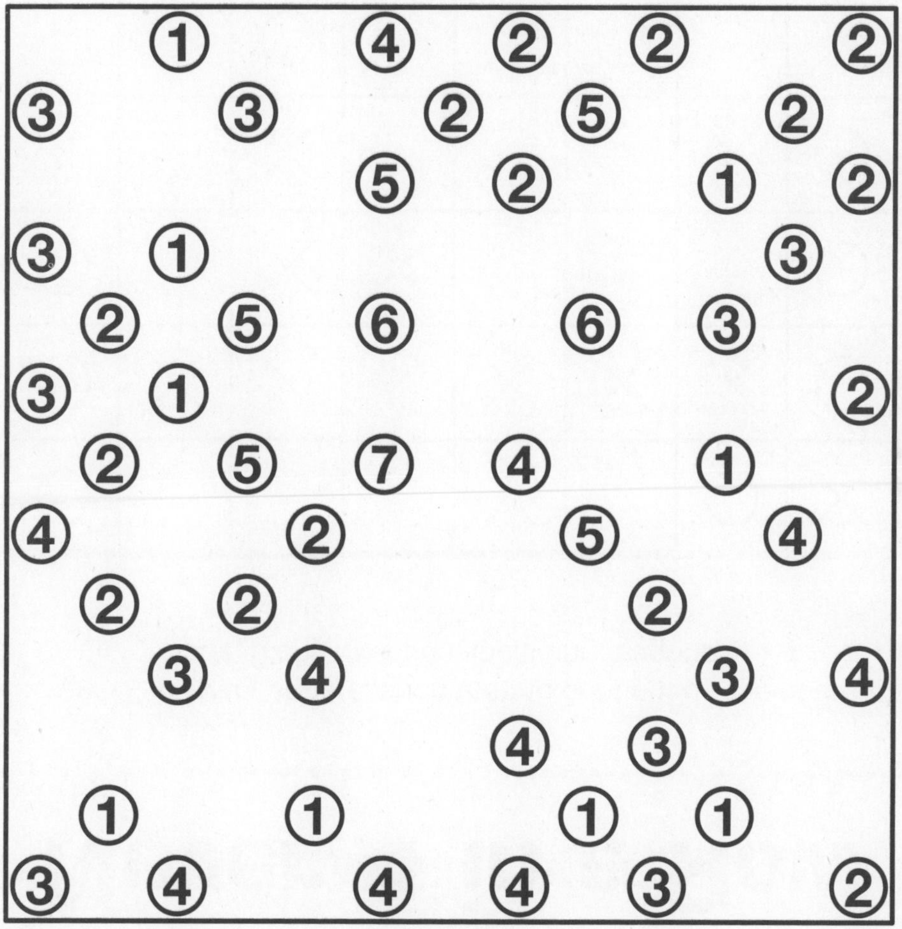

Never 4 in a Row

Place an 'X' or an 'O' in every square, such that no continuous line of four 'X's or 'O's is made in any direction, including diagonally.

O				X		O	X
O	X	X		X	X	X	O
O		X	X				O
		X				X	O
		O		X	O		X
X		X		X	X	O	O
X		X	X			X	O
X	X	O	O	X		X	O

Slitherlink

Draw a single loop by connecting dots with horizontal and vertical lines so that each numbered square has the specified number of adjacent line segments. The loop cannot cross or touch itself at any point.

	0		2			3	
0		1	2		2		
	0		2		3	2	1
			0	2		3	
	0		2	2			
3	1	1		1		2	
		1		2	2		3
	2			2		3	

Codeword

Each number in this grid represents a different letter. Solve the code to create a complete crossword grid, using only English words (no proper nouns or abbreviations).

You can use the table beneath the grid to keep track of the code, and can cross off used letters along both sides of the grid.

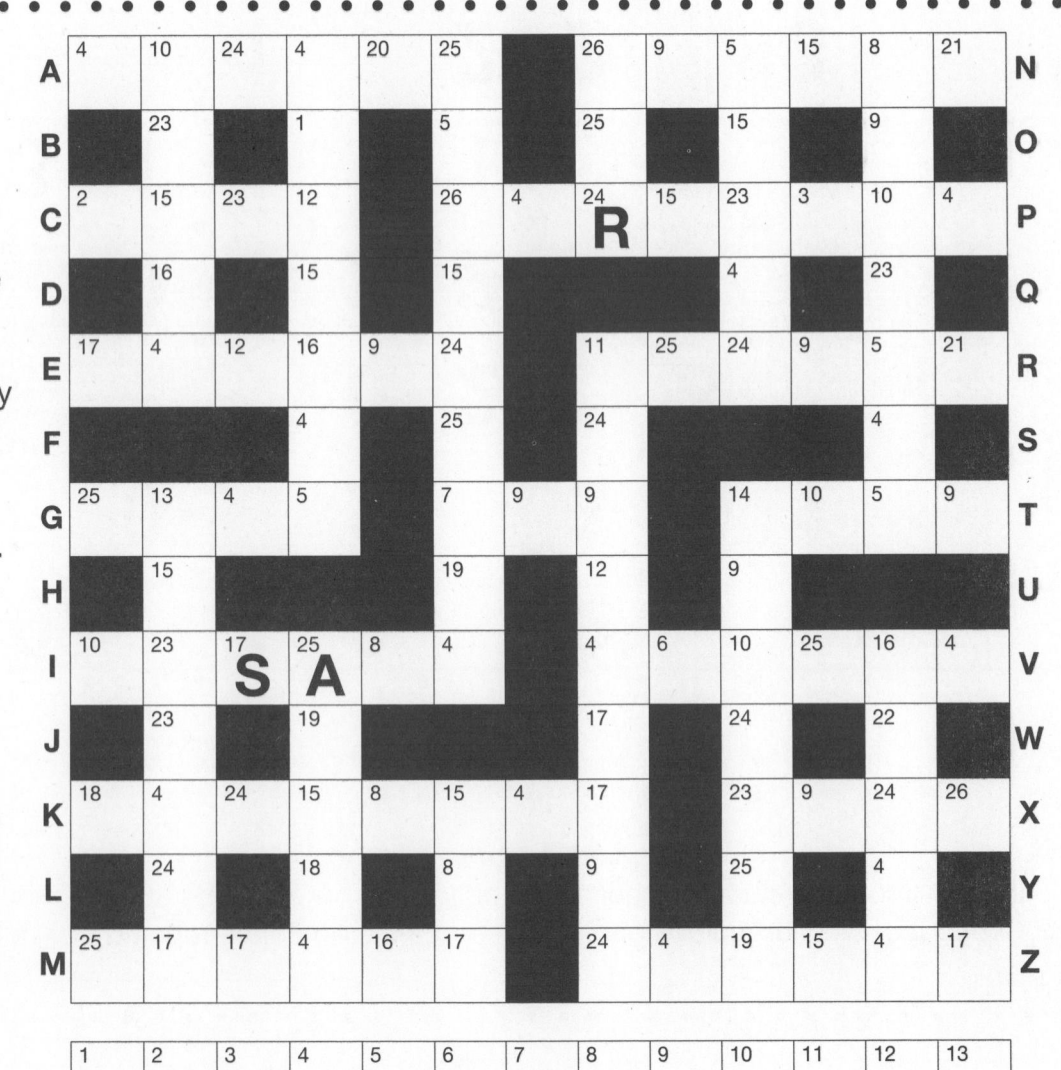

A	4	10	24	4	20	25	■	26	9	5	15	8	21	N
B	■	23	■	1	■	5	■	25	■	15	■	9	■	O
C	2	15	23	12	■	26	4	24 R	15	23	3	10	4	P
D	■	16	■	15	■	15	■	■	■	4	■	23	■	Q
E	17	4	12	16	9	24	■	11	25	24	9	5	21	R
F	■	■	■	4	■	25	■	24	■	■	■	4	■	S
G	25	13	4	5	■	7	9	9	■	14	10	5	9	T
H	■	15	■	■	■	19	■	12	■	9	■	■	■	U
I	10	23	17 S	25 A	8	4	■	4	6	10	25	16	4	V
J	■	23	■	19	■	■	■	17	■	24	■	22	■	W
K	18	4	24	15	8	15	4	17	■	23	9	24	26	X
L	■	24	■	18	■	8	■	9	■	25	■	4	■	Y
M	25	17	17	4	16	17	■	24	4	19	15	4	17	Z

1	2	3	4	5	6	7	8	9	10	11	12	13
14	15	16	17	18	19	20	21	22	23	24	25	26

Rectangles

Draw rectangles along the grid lines so that each number ends up in a rectangle containing exactly that many cells. Each cell must be in exactly one rectangle – so rectangles cannot overlap.

									3
3	16								
				4					
2	2				4	2		4	
					6				
			7					4	
				21					
									6
4	4								
						5			3

Kakuro

Place a number in the range 1–9 into every white cell, so that every horizontal run of white cells adds up to the number given to its left, and every vertical run of white cells adds up to the number given above it. No number can be repeated within a run.

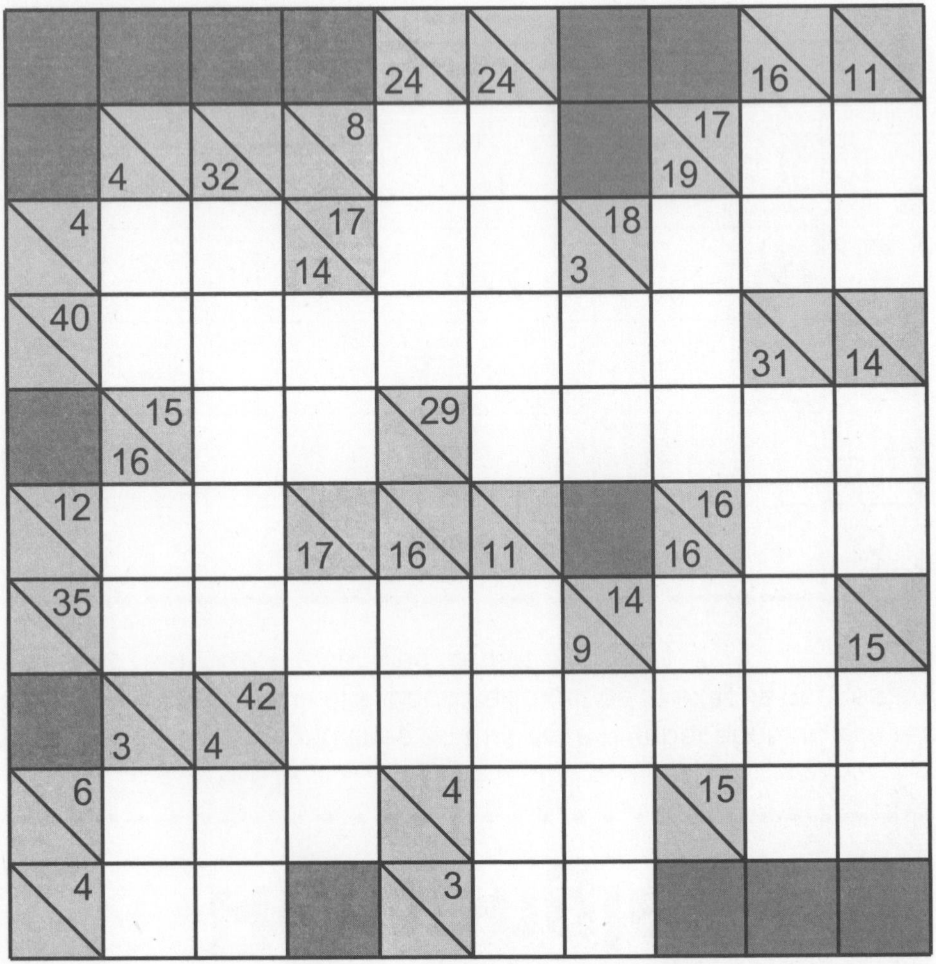

110

Futoshiki

Place 1 to 8 once each into every row and column while obeying the inequality signs. Less than ('<') and greater than ('>') signs between some squares indicate that the values in these two squares must be greater than, or less than, one another, as indicated by the sign.

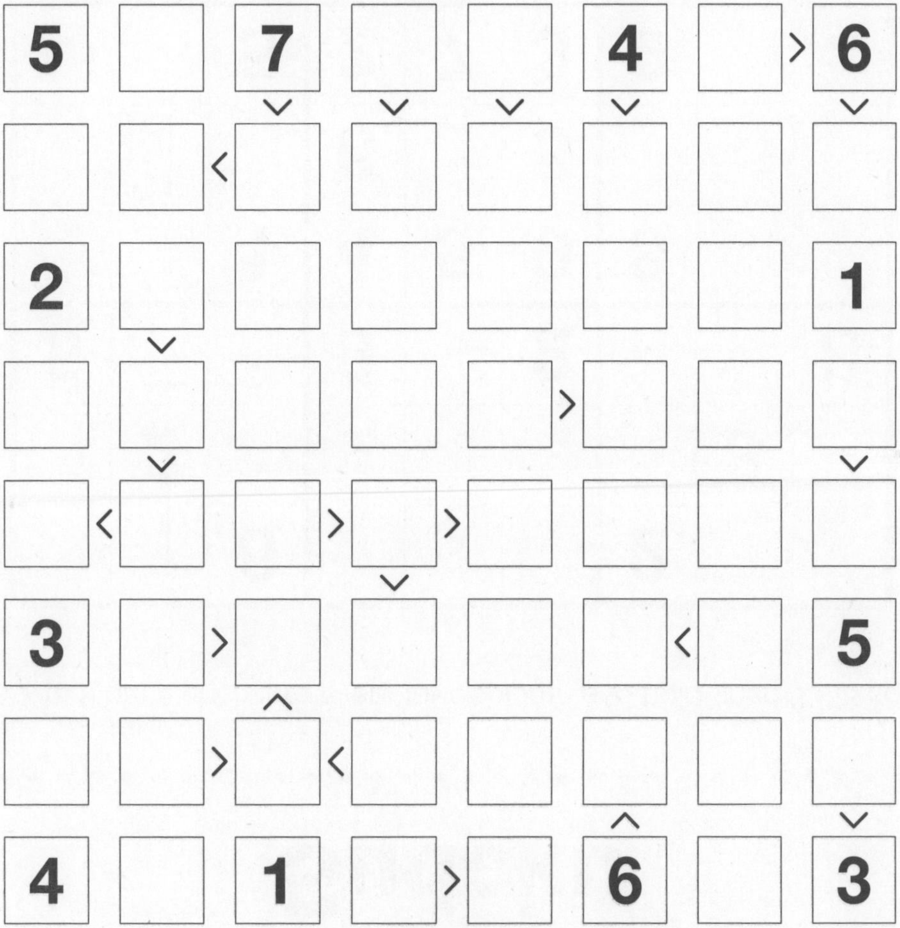

Sudoku

Place 1 to 9 once each into every row, column and bold-lined 3 × 3 square.

		6				2		
	2						3	
5			9		2			8
		1	4	5	9	8		
			6		8			
		5	2	7	3	9		
9			3		7			5
	8						1	
		3				6		

Letter Circle

Can you find the nine-letter word hidden in this Letter Circle? Form words by using the centre letter and a combination of two or more other letters from the circle. How many other words can you find?

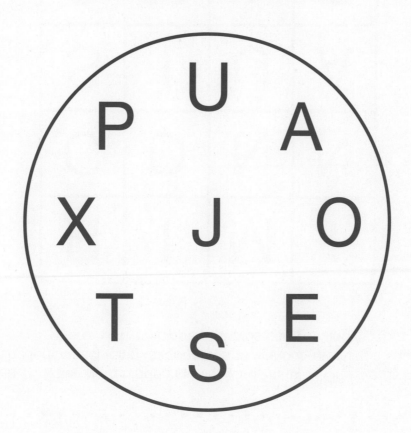

U

P A

X J O

T E

S

Word Square

Can you find the 16-letter word hidden in this Word Square? Find words by moving from letter to touching letter, excluding diagonally, and without revisiting a square in a single word. How many other words can you find?

R	I	M	I
C	D	N	N
S	I	U	A
G	N	I	T

Crossword

Across

1 Tennis and soccer, for example (6)
4 Move apart (6)
8 Afore (3)
9 Flawed (9)
11 Fortune (4)
12 Obliquely (8)
15 Public declaration of intent (9)
18 Disturb (8)
19 Selves (4)
21 Model (9)
23 Credit note (inits) (3)
24 Shove (6)
25 Air current (6)

Down

1 Olfacts (6)
2 Conquers (9)
3 Journey (4)
5 Contrary (8)
6 Look at (3)
7 Hate (6)
10 Sorely (9)
13 Next to (9)
14 Smarmy (8)
16 Marionette (6)
17 Take for granted (6)
20 Alcoholic malt drink (4)
22 Blade (3)

Comedians

Find each of the listed items in this wordsearch puzzle. They can be written forwards or backwards in any direction, including diagonally.

BRAND
BREMNER
COHEN
CONNOLLY
DAWSON
EDMONDSON
ENFIELD
HANCOCK
HARDY
JONES
LAUREL
MARTIN
MERTON
MILLIGAN
MOORE
MORECAMBE
REEVES
SAUNDERS
SEINFELD
WILLIAMS

M	B	L	S	E	I	N	A	A	O	F	A	E	S	K	E	F
R	T	R	A	E	S	M	L	H	A	I	D	N	M	L	S	S
N	M	I	L	L	I	G	A	N	A	M	S	O	E	M	I	E
U	E	Y	R	M	O	N	L	R	O	I	R	B	E	O	M	L
I	L	E	L	L	C	F	F	B	T	S	E	R	O	R	O	S
M	N	V	O	O	D	O	L	E	R	I	D	A	N	E	M	C
R	W	Y	C	N	R	R	Y	L	L	O	N	N	O	C	W	S
T	M	K	W	O	E	E	A	A	D	D	U	D	O	A	S	O
O	V	S	L	O	S	M	H	V	A	I	A	L	N	M	D	B
H	M	O	E	M	O	E	E	S	J	W	S	E	A	B	D	E
O	D	D	S	Y	E	R	N	R	S	R	B	I	V	E	A	E
F	L	R	S	D	R	O	E	O	E	R	L	F	N	L	Y	R
C	C	M	E	R	T	O	N	E	J	L	E	N	I	E	S	L
S	C	S	O	A	J	M	E	O	I	B	R	E	M	N	E	R
K	L	O	F	H	S	R	E	W	L	B	U	H	V	N	V	M
O	R	A	F	E	W	N	E	B	E	O	A	O	M	E	D	C
N	V	R	I	B	C	I	E	N	E	T	L	C	E	Y	S	N

Jigsaw Sudoku

Place 1 to 9 once each into every row, column and bold-lined jigsaw shape of this puzzle.

			7					5
			1					
							1	
		6		2		4	8	9
		8				7		
4	5	3		7		8		
	8							
					6			
3					7			

Going Round in Circles

Can you find a path through the maze, entering at the top and exiting at the bottom?

Number Link

Draw horizontal and vertical lines to form a set of paths, each connecting a pair of identical numbers. All numbers must be used. No more than one line can pass through any square.

						1		2	
	3			4				5	
		6		7					
		8				9			
	3							5	
							10	2	
6			7				11		10
8			9	4			1		11

Calcudoku

Place 1 to 8 once each into every row and column; while obeying the clues. The value at the top left of each bold-lined region must result when the numbers in that region have the given operation (+, -, ×, ÷) applied between them. For - and ÷ operations, start with the largest number in the region and then subtract or divide by the remaining numbers.

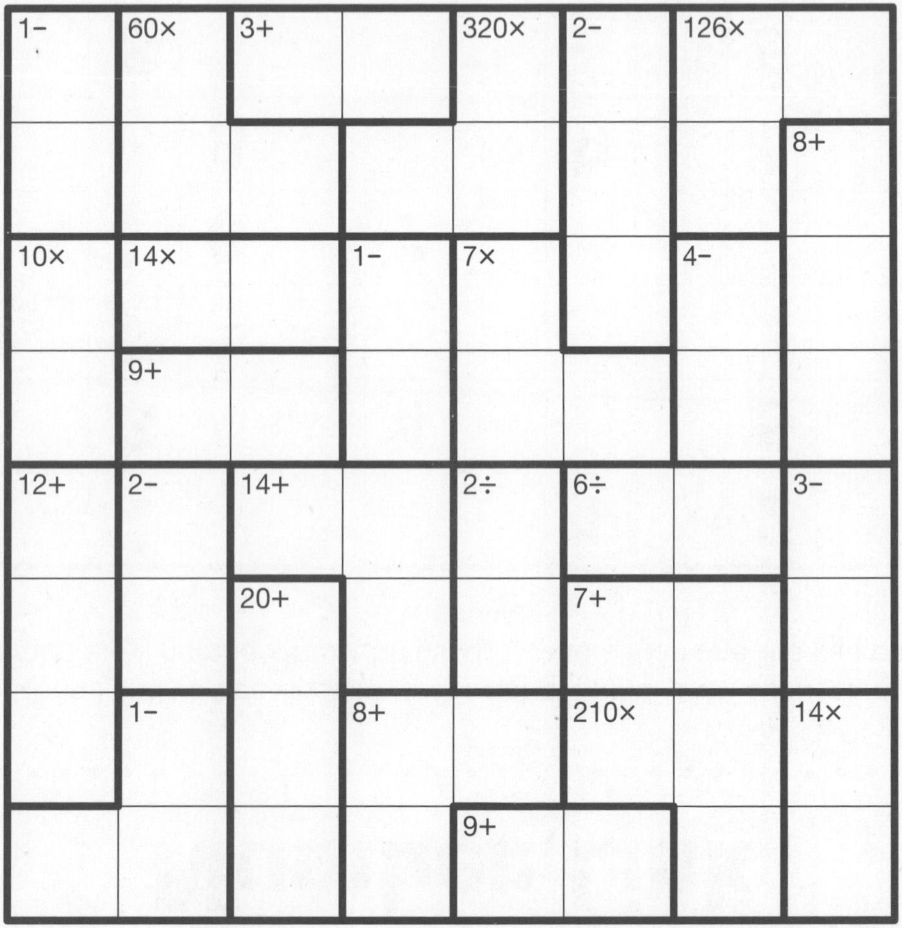

Bridges

Join circled numbers with horizontal or vertical lines so that each number has the given number of connecting lines. No more than two lines may join any pair of numbers, and lines cannot cross. The finished layout must allow you to travel from any number to any other number just by following one or more lines.

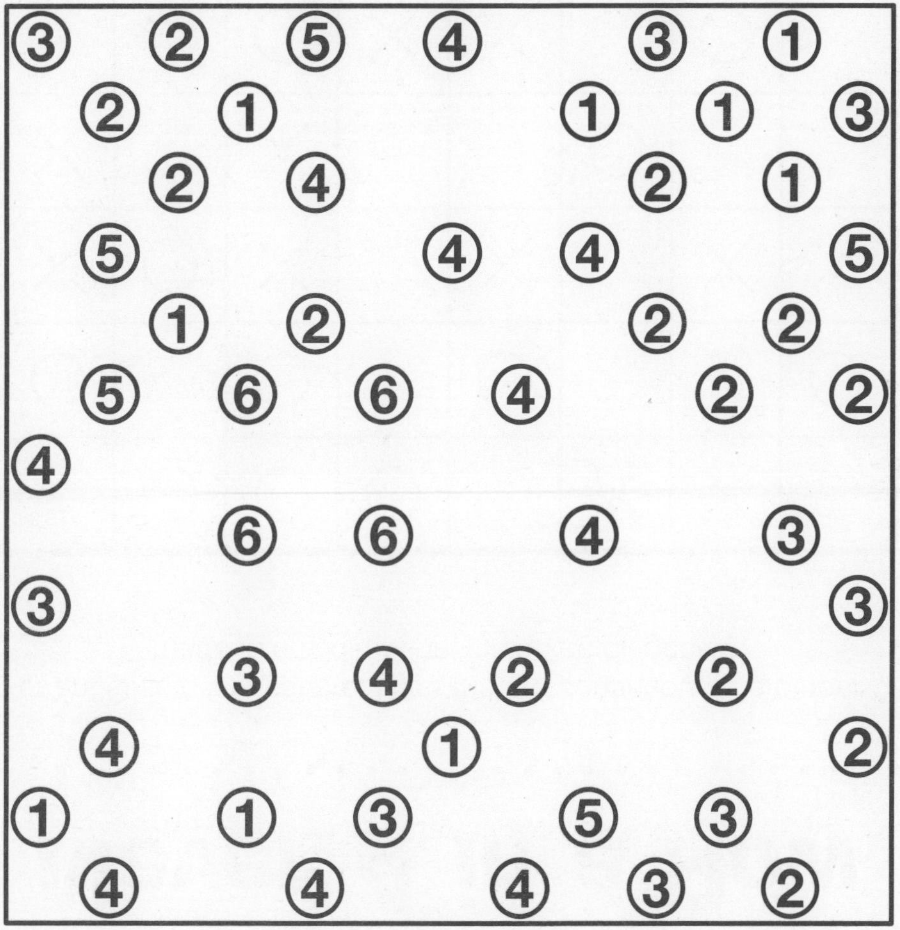

Never 4 in a Row

Place an 'X' or an 'O' in every square, such that no continuous line of four 'X's or 'O's is made in any direction, including diagonally.

	O	O	O		X	X	
O		O		O			O
X	O	X		X		X	X
X		X			O		
	O	O	X	X		O	
X	X	O	O				
X	O		O	O	X		O
X	O			X			X

Slitherlink

Draw a single loop by connecting dots with horizontal and vertical lines so that each numbered square has the specified number of adjacent line segments. The loop cannot cross or touch itself at any point.

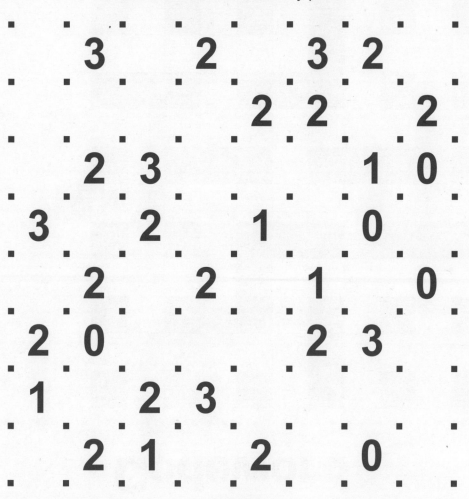

	3		2		3	2	
				2	2		2
	2	3				1	0
3		2		1		0	
	2		2		1		0
2	0				2	3	
1		2	3				
	2	1		2		0	

Codeword

Each number in this grid represents a different letter. Solve the code to create a complete crossword grid, using only English words (no proper nouns or abbreviations).

You can use the table beneath the grid to keep track of the code, and can cross off used letters along both sides of the grid.

A	19	■	17	■	22	■	17	■	22	■	23	■	17	N
B	21	15	13	19 T	15	13	1	■	17	7	17	2	19	O
C	17	■	18	■	16	■	16	■	14	■	10	■	21	P
D	13	16	12	16	2	■	5	2	15	10	10	11	16	Q
E	4	■	21	■	8	■	■	■	13	■	■	■	15	R
F	■	13 N	16	24	16	2	19	21	16	11	16	26	26	S
G	17	■	2	■	■	■	15	■	■	■	13	■	14	T
H	8	25	16	22	22	15	8	15	16	13	19	26 S	■	U
I	8	■	■	■	25	■	■	■	9	■	15	■	11	V
J	6	13	16	20	6	17	11	■	7	17	2	26	16	W
K	26	■	6	■	1	■	25	■	15	■	16	■	17	X
L	16	17	2	19	21	■	1	17	2	3	11	16	26	Y
M	5	■	25	■	19	■	25	■	16	■	18	■	16	Z

1	2	3	4	5	6	7	8	9	10	11	12	13
14	15	16	17	18	19	20	21	22	23	24	25	26

Rectangles

Draw rectangles along the grid lines so that each number ends up in a rectangle containing exactly that many cells. Each cell must be in exactly one rectangle – so rectangles cannot overlap.

			6			25			
	7		8	6	6				3
			3						
9				6		6			
								5	
		3					5		2

Kakuro

Place a number in the range 1–9 into every white cell, so that every horizontal run of white cells adds up to the number given to its left, and every vertical run of white cells adds up to the number given above it. No number can be repeated within a run.

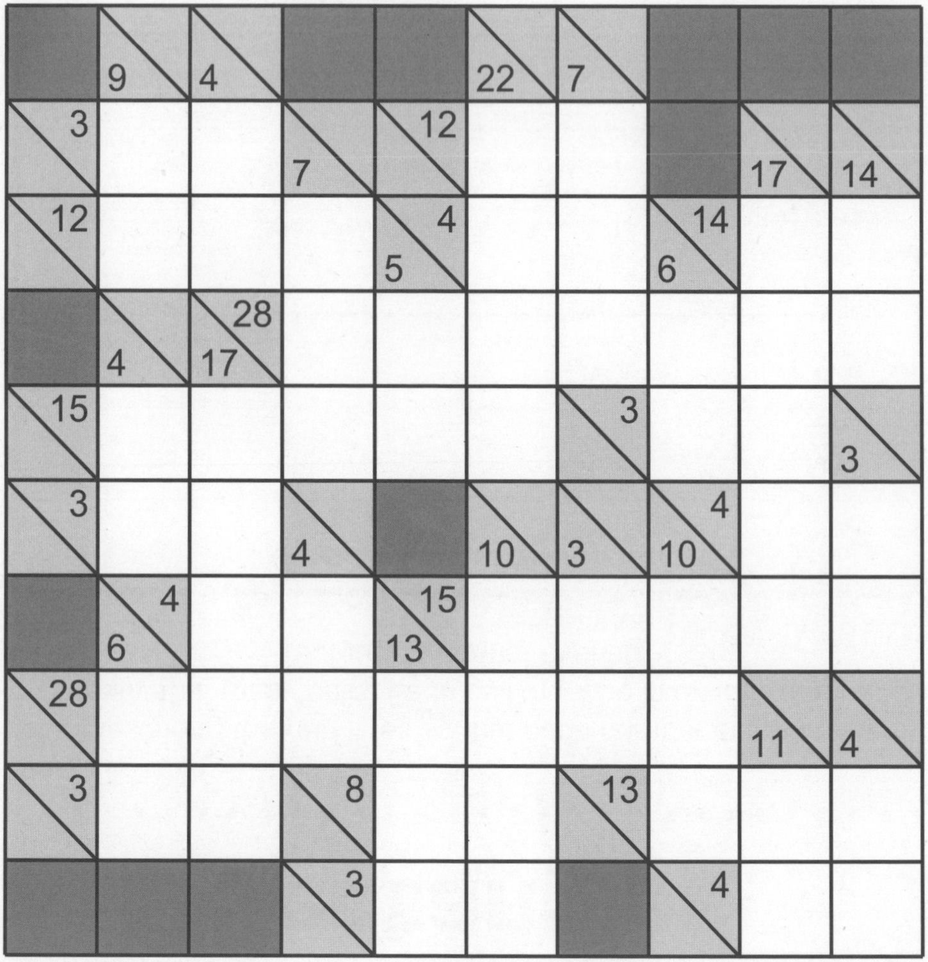

Futoshiki

Place 1 to 8 once each into every row and column while obeying the inequality signs. Less than ('<') and greater than ('>') signs between some squares indicate that the values in these two squares must be greater than, or less than, one another, as indicated by the sign.

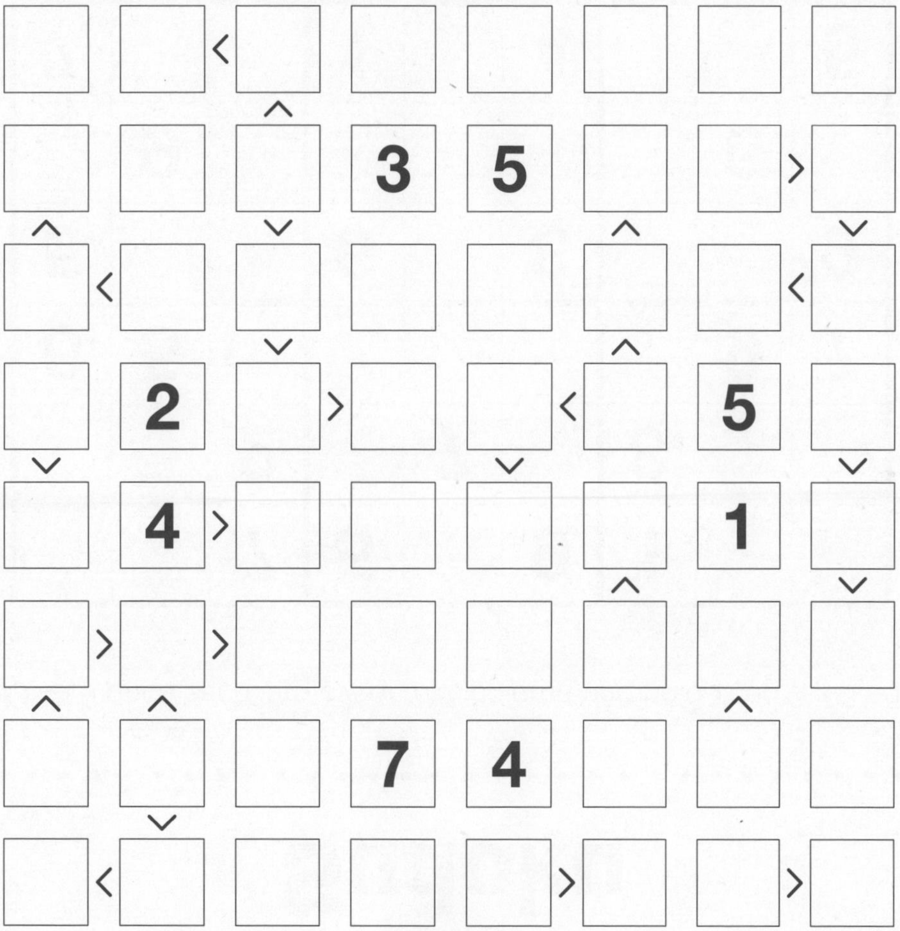

Sudoku

Place 1 to 9 once each into every row, column and bold-lined 3 × 3 square.

		7	5		9	1		
		2		7		8		
6	5						9	7
5			6		8			9
	9						6	
7			1		4			5
8	6						7	1
		5		6		9		
		4	9		1	6		

Letter Circle

Can you find the nine-letter word hidden in this Letter Circle? Form words by using the centre letter and a combination of two or more other letters from the circle. How many other words can you find?

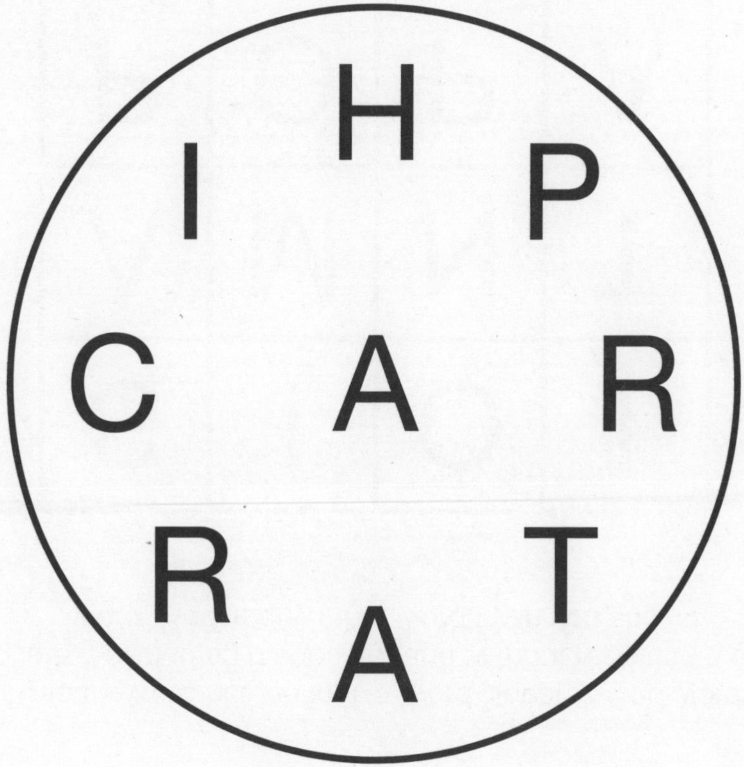

Word Square

Can you find the 16-letter word hidden in this Word Square? Find words by moving from letter to touching letter, excluding diagonally, and without revisiting a square in a single word. How many other words can you find?

S	I	O	I
A	M	N	T
P	O	P	A
P	R	R	I

Crossword

Across

7 Ghost (7)
9 Sound (5)
10 Adam's mate (3)
11 Emission (9)
12 Bop (5)
14 Chewed the fat (7)
16 Most profound (7)
18 Military trainee (5)
19 Receivers (9)
20 Centre (3)
21 Belonging to them (5)
22 Tobacco consumers (7)

Down

1 Added on (8)
2 Foundation (4)
3 Two-channel audio (6)
4 Tropical fruit (6)
5 Allowed entry (8)
6 Ripped (4)
8 Drugs (11)
13 Draws (8)
15 Information store (8)
17 Send abroad (6)
18 Habit (6)
19 Rodents (4)
20 Take notice of (4)

Strong Emotions

Find each of the listed items in this wordsearch puzzle. They can be written forwards or backwards in any direction, including diagonally.

- ABHORRENCE
- ANGER
- ANNOYANCE
- AWE
- DELIGHT
- DEPRESSION
- DESIRE
- DESPAIR
- DISAPPOINTMENT
- DISMAY
- EMPATHY
- HOSTILITY
- JEALOUSY
- JOY
- LOATHING
- REGRET
- REPUGNANCE
- SADNESS
- SURPRISE
- WONDER

S	L	N	A	R	T	A	T	H	G	I	L	E	D	N	I	R
O	D	O	T	L	O	I	N	R	B	N	S	S	R	R	O	R
N	I	T	D	C	E	J	E	A	L	O	U	S	Y	L	L	T
N	R	I	N	T	A	D	M	P	R	R	Y	Y	H	S	G	S
Y	I	A	W	S	N	C	T	A	P	A	H	E	T	N	U	I
D	A	D	I	O	D	P	N	R	B	M	T	D	A	M	H	E
Y	N	I	W	E	G	N	I	H	T	A	O	L	P	D	E	N
J	N	N	S	E	N	S	O	E	W	H	R	H	M	D	A	Y
N	O	I	S	S	E	R	P	E	D	C	A	S	E	H	U	T
N	Y	Y	D	O	R	E	P	Y	E	T	R	S	D	L	Y	D
I	A	S	N	E	C	N	A	N	G	U	P	E	R	T	L	L
S	N	P	N	N	P	M	S	N	H	A	S	N	G	D	E	E
E	C	C	H	O	S	T	I	L	I	T	Y	D	A	R	I	N
P	E	R	R	I	G	P	D	R	E	G	N	A	I	I	E	A
S	M	M	D	D	W	L	N	Y	R	E	A	S	D	N	N	T
H	O	G	A	P	N	G	O	G	P	J	E	N	E	P	D	S
D	I	E	E	E	G	L	S	E	H	D	A	O	R	R	A	J

Jigsaw Sudoku

Place 1 to 9 once each into every row, column and bold-lined jigsaw shape of this puzzle.

2								
8		9				5		
	6	1				3		
							9	
			7		5			
	8							
		8				7	2	
		3				4		5
								3

Going Round in Circles

Can you find a path through the maze, entering at the top and exiting at the bottom?

Number Link

Draw horizontal and vertical lines to form a set of paths, each connecting a pair of identical numbers. All numbers must be used. No more than one line can pass through any square.

1					2				
						3			
	4	5		6		1	5		
		7				8	9		
				10					
6									
4						8			2
7		9		10					3

Calcudoku

Place 1 to 8 once each into every row and column, while obeying the clues. The value at the top left of each bold-lined region must result when the numbers in that region have the given operation (+, -, ×, ÷) applied between them. For - and ÷ operations, start with the largest number in the region and then subtract or divide by the remaining numbers.

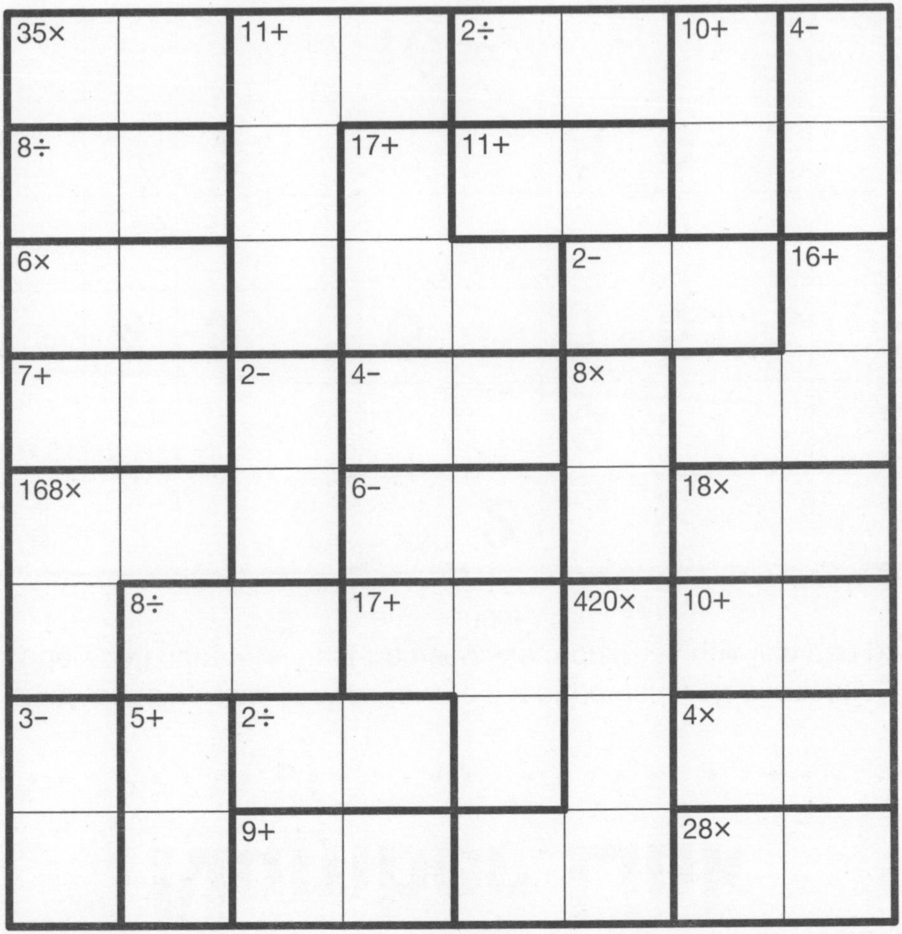

Bridges

Join circled numbers with horizontal or vertical lines so that each number has the given number of connecting lines. No more than two lines may join any pair of numbers, and lines cannot cross. The finished layout must allow you to travel from any number to any other number just by following one or more lines.

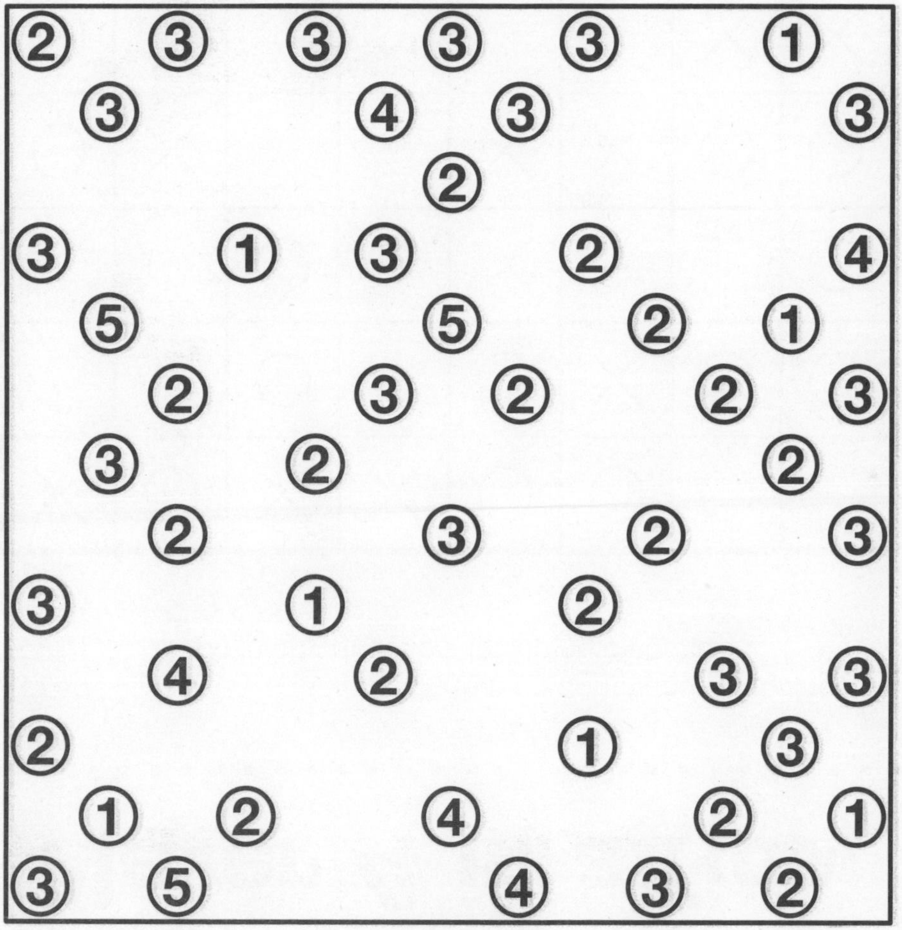

Never 4 in a Row

Place an 'X' or an 'O' in every square, such that no continuous line of four 'X's or 'O's is made in any direction, including diagonally.

X	O	X	X	O	O	O	
	X	O		O	X	O	O
		O		X			O
O	X			X	X	O	O
O						X	X
	O	O	X	X			O
X	O	X	O		X	X	X
O		O	O	O	X		X

Slitherlink

Draw a single loop by connecting dots with horizontal and vertical lines so that each numbered square has the specified number of adjacent line segments. The loop cannot cross or touch itself at any point.

			3	2		3	
	2				0	2	
3		3		1		3	
1		1		3		1	
	3		1		1		1
	3		1		3		1
	2	1				3	
	1		3	2			

Codeword

Each number in this grid represents a different letter. Solve the code to create a complete crossword grid, using only English words (no proper nouns or abbreviations).

You can use the table beneath the grid to keep track of the code, and can cross off used letters along both sides of the grid.

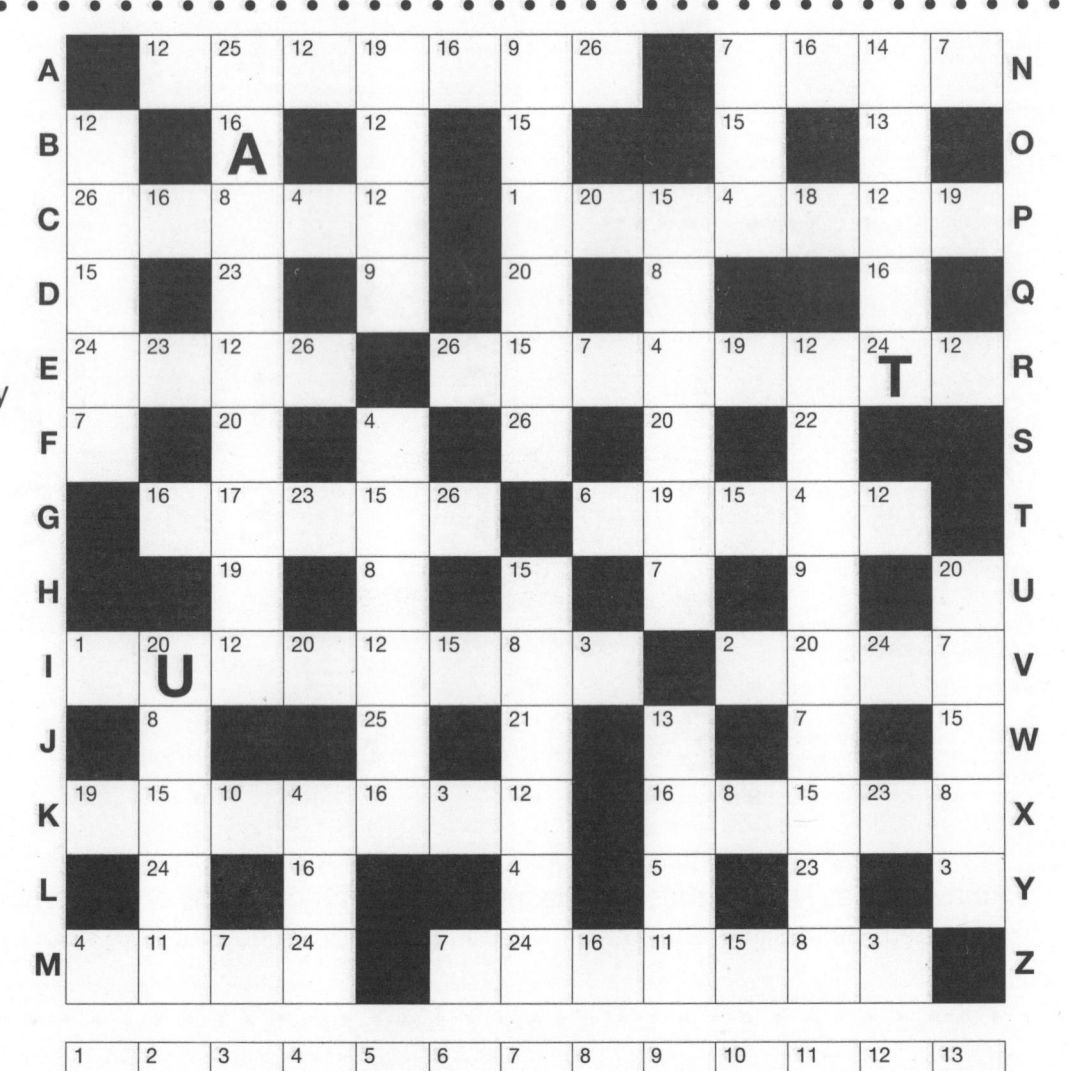

A	■	12	25	12	19	16	9	26	■	7	16	14	7	N
B	12	■	16 A	■	12	■	15	■	■	15	■	13	■	O
C	26	16	8	4	12	■	1	20	15	4	18	12	19	P
D	15	■	23	■	9	■	20	■	8	■	■	16	■	Q
E	24	23	12	26	■	26	15	7	4	19	12	24 T	12	R
F	7	■	20	■	4	■	26	■	20	■	22	■	■	S
G	■	16	17	23	15	26	■	6	19	15	4	12	■	T
H	■	■	19	■	8	■	15	■	7	■	9	■	20	U
I	1	20 U	12	20	12	15	8	3	■	2	20	24	7	V
J	■	8	■	■	25	■	21	■	13	■	7	■	15	W
K	19	15	10	4	16	3	12	■	16	8	15	23	8	X
L	■	24	■	16	■	■	4	■	5	■	23	■	3	Y
M	4	11	7	24	■	7	24	16	11	15	8	3	■	Z

1	2	3	4	5	6	7	8	9	10	11	12	13
14	15	16	17	18	19	20	21	22	23	24	25	26

Rectangles

Draw rectangles along the grid lines so that each number ends up in a rectangle containing exactly that many cells. Each cell must be in exactly one rectangle – so rectangles cannot overlap.

	8			3					15
2									
	6			3					
6		5				5	14		4
	3								
		8	4	8					3
					3				

Kakuro

Place a number in the range 1–9 into every white cell, so that every horizontal run of white cells adds up to the number given to its left, and every vertical run of white cells adds up to the number given above it. No number can be repeated within a run.

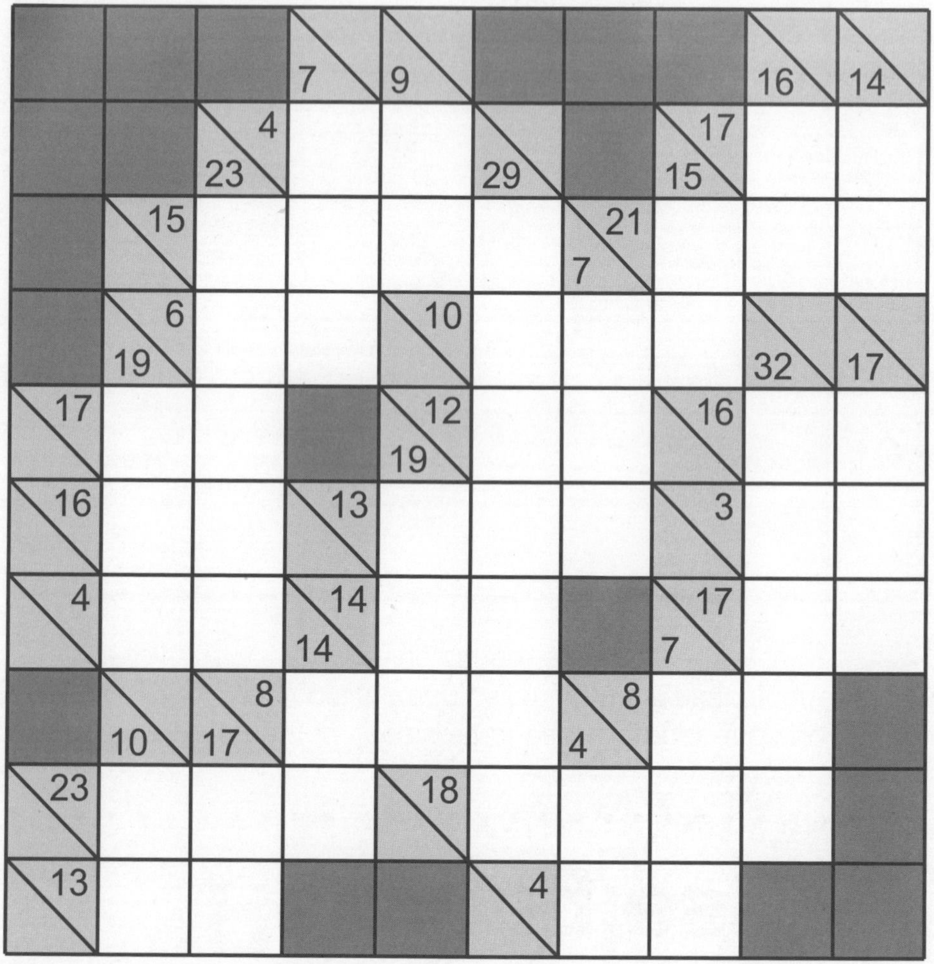

Futoshiki

Place 1 to 8 once each into every row and column while obeying the inequality signs. Less than ('<') and greater than ('>') signs between some squares indicate that the values in these two squares must be greater than, or less than, one another, as indicated by the sign.

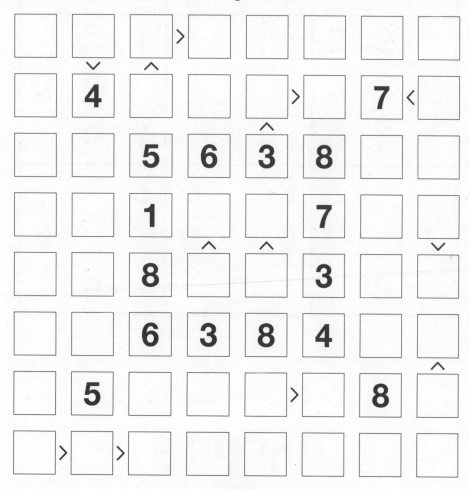

					>									
		∨		∧										
		4							>			7	<	
								∧						
				5		6		3		8				
				1						7				
						∧		∧						∨
				8						3				
				6		3		8		4				
														∧
		5							>			8		
	>		>											

Sudoku

Place 1 to 9 once each into every row, column and bold-lined 3 × 3 square.

	9			8			3	
4			5		6			2
		2	9		3	7		
	5	4				6	2	
3								8
	2	1				3	5	
		3	8		5	9		
6			4		9			1
	4			2			6	

Letter Circle

Can you find the nine-letter word hidden in this Letter Circle? Form words by using the centre letter and a combination of two or more other letters from the circle. How many other words can you find?

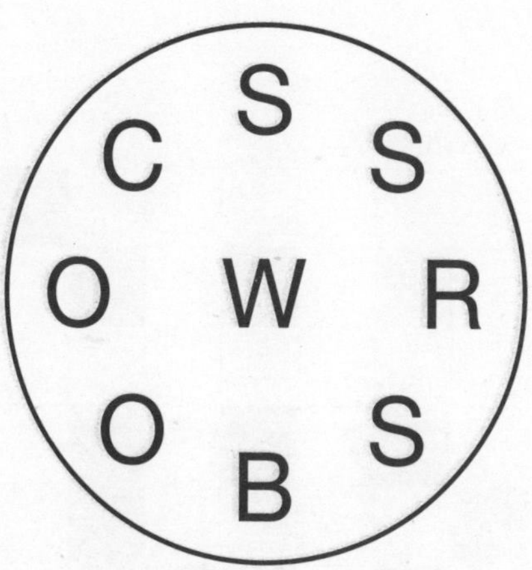

Word Square

Can you find the 16-letter word hidden in this Word Square? Find words by moving from letter to touching letter, excluding diagonally, and without revisiting a square in a single word. How many other words can you find?

E	N	T	I
V	N	N	O
U	O	A	Y
N	C	L	L

Crossword

Across

1 Simple facts (6)
4 Northern European sea (6)
9 Hearsay (7)
10 Straighten up (5)
11 Clothed (4)
12 Type of soft cheese (7)
14 Unwind (6)
16 Outfit for school sports (3,3)
19 Seer (7)
21 Satellite (4)
23 Exhibited (5)
24 Intoxicated (7)
25 Group of programmes (6)
26 Silhouette (6)

Down

1 Given birth to (4)
2 Taster (7)
3 Was able (5)
5 Disorder (7)
6 Turnabout (5)
7 Gets in touch with (8)
8 Visitors to a website (5)
13 Reckons (8)
15 Improve (7)
17 Rapped on a door (7)
18 Examine (5)
20 Smell (5)
21 Orifice (5)
22 Again (4)

Breeds of Sheep

Find each of the listed items in this wordsearch puzzle. They can be written forwards or backwards in any direction, including diagonally.

BORERAY
CHAROLLAIS
CHEVIOT
COOPWORTH
COTSWOLD
DALESBRED
DARTMOOR
EXMOOR HORN
HEBRIDEAN
HERDWICK
KERRY HILL
LACAUNE
ORKNEY
ROUGH FELL
RYELAND
SHETLAND
SOAY
TEESWATER
WELSH MOUNTAIN
WILTSHIRE HORN

A	H	H	L	E	K	A	A	B	N	L	O	O	B	E	R	A
A	X	O	D	T	Y	C	O	D	L	O	W	S	T	O	C	P
H	T	K	F	O	I	A	I	R	W	I	Y	A	O	S	T	I
T	S	E	H	L	W	L	R	W	K	H	O	M	I	I	T	O
H	H	B	A	H	O	E	E	E	D	N	T	E	Y	A	M	W
T	E	L	T	L	L	I	H	Y	R	R	E	K	N	L	E	H
R	T	B	D	H	A	T	I	A	A	O	E	Y	W	L	M	W
O	L	A	R	A	O	L	R	D	K	H	B	H	S	O	I	T
W	A	K	W	I	L	T	S	H	I	R	E	H	O	R	N	S
P	N	C	V	L	D	E	A	A	E	O	M	N	O	A	R	I
O	D	E	U	Y	E	E	S	T	W	O	W	D	E	H	W	N
O	H	H	C	O	C	E	A	B	U	M	B	A	L	C	H	A
C	T	H	B	C	E	W	S	N	R	X	E	R	H	O	E	L
A	U	T	O	I	S	R	T	L	L	E	F	H	G	U	O	R
U	H	R	Y	E	L	A	N	D	O	L	D	I	O	L	U	A
N	T	R	E	A	I	R	W	D	E	S	W	V	W	A	H	I
A	T	T	E	N	U	A	C	A	L	N	W	L	R	Y	L	B

Jigsaw Sudoku

Place 1 to 9 once each into every row, column and bold-lined jigsaw shape of this puzzle.

	5	8				6		
	6	1		2				
1			6			4	8	
	2	5			3			1
				4		8	6	
		9				2	3	

Going Round in Circles

Can you find a path through the maze, entering at the top and exiting at the bottom?

Number Link

Draw horizontal and vertical lines to form a set of paths, each connecting a pair of identical numbers. All numbers must be used. No more than one line can pass through any square.

1		2		3				4	3
5					6				
	7						4		8
		5							
	7						2		
						1	9		
								6	
	10				10	8			
									9

Calcudoku

Place 1 to 8 once each into every row and column, while obeying the clues. The value at the top left of each bold-lined region must result when the numbers in that region have the given operation (+, -, ×, ÷) applied between them. For - and ÷ operations, start with the largest number in the region and then subtract or divide by the remaining numbers.

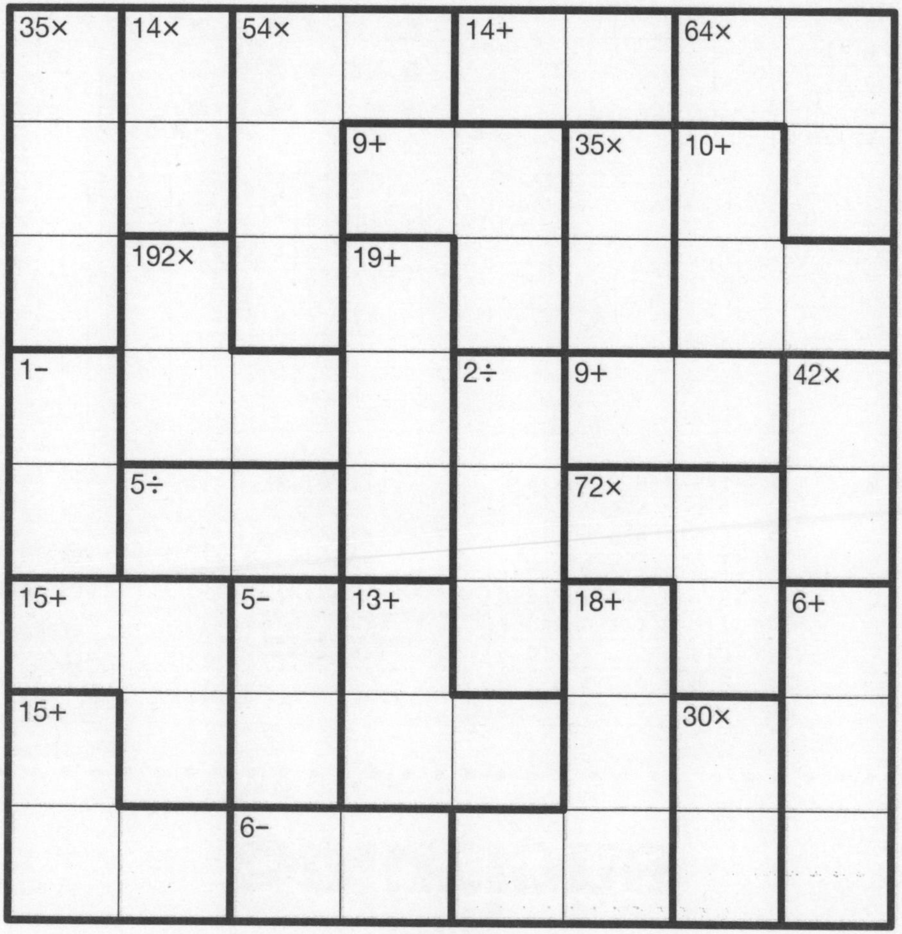

Solutions

3

4

5

6	7	2	5	9	3	1	4	8
8	1	6	3	5	7	4	9	2
9	2	4	1	7	5	8	6	3
4	6	8	9	1	2	5	3	7
3	8	9	4	2	1	6	7	5
7	5	3	8	4	6	9	2	1
5	4	7	2	6	8	3	1	9
1	9	5	7	3	4	2	8	6
2	3	1	6	8	9	7	5	4

6

7

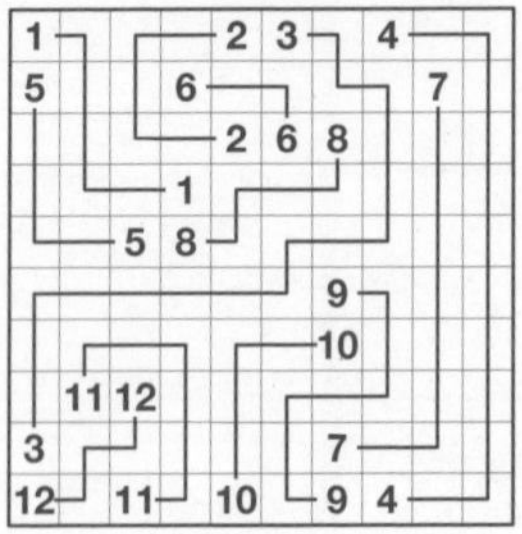

8

9

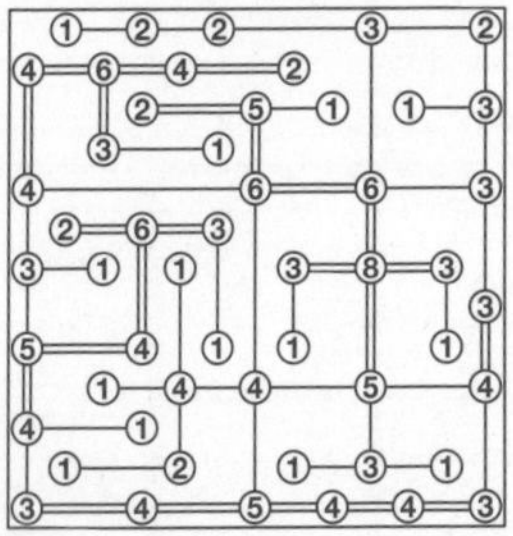

10

O	X	O	X	O	X	X	O
O	O	O	X	X	X	O	X
O	X	X	O	X	O	O	O
X	O	O	O	X	O	X	O
X	O	X	O	O	O	X	O
X	O	O	X	O	X	X	X
O	X	X	O	X	X	O	O
O	O	X	O	X	O	X	O

11

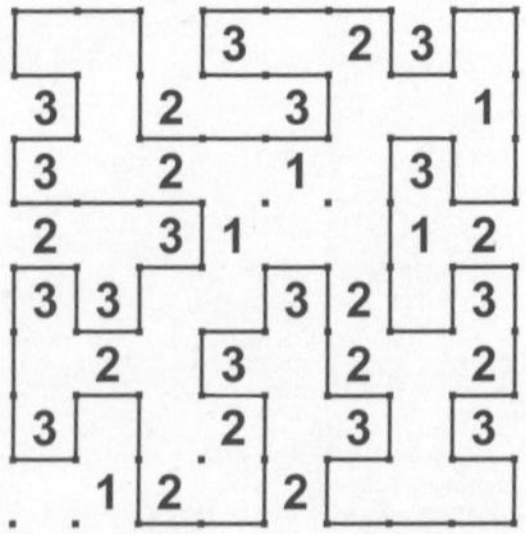

12

13

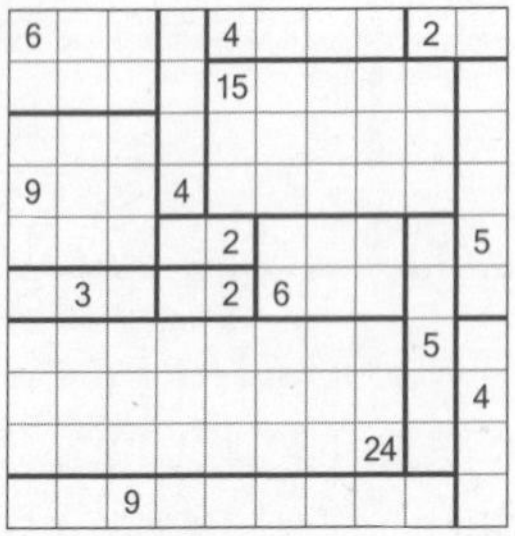

14

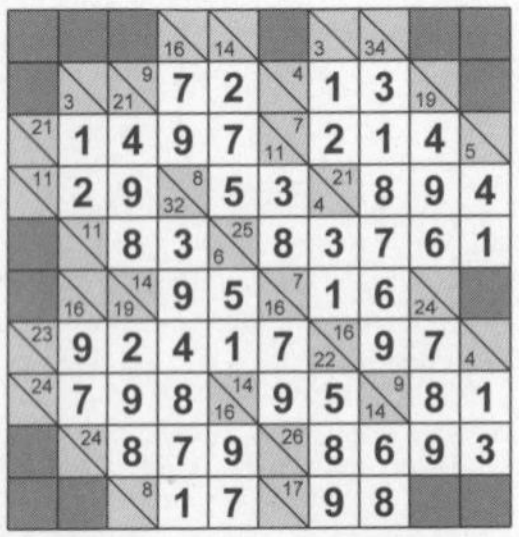

15

16

5	9	6	4	2	8	1	7	3
3	7	8	9	1	6	2	5	4
4	2	1	3	7	5	9	6	8
1	8	9	6	4	2	7	3	5
6	4	7	5	9	3	8	2	1
2	5	3	7	8	1	6	4	9
7	3	4	8	6	9	5	1	2
9	6	2	1	5	4	3	8	7
8	1	5	2	3	7	4	9	6

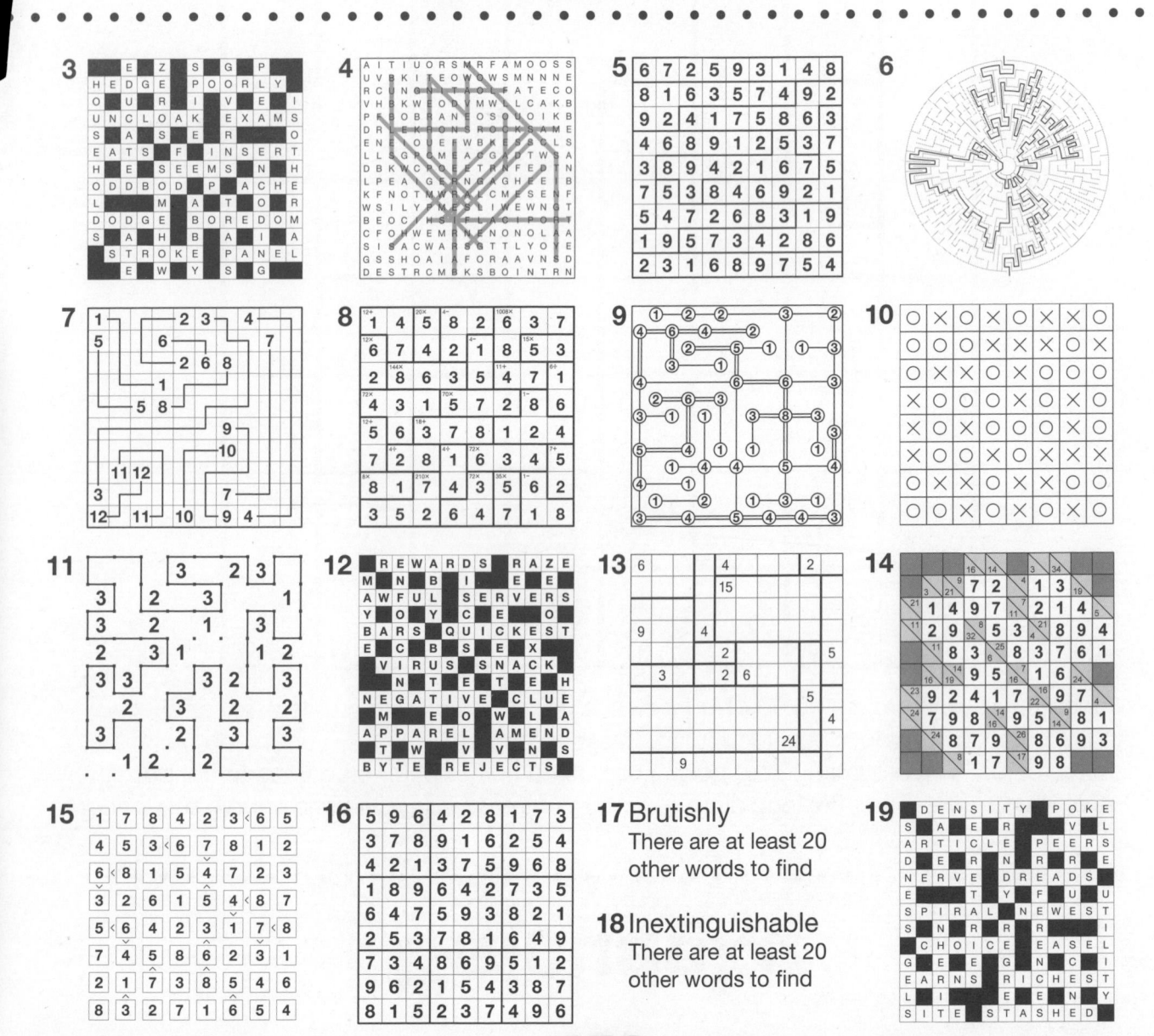

17 Brutishly
There are at least 20 other words to find

18 Inextinguishable
There are at least 20 other words to find

19

Solutions

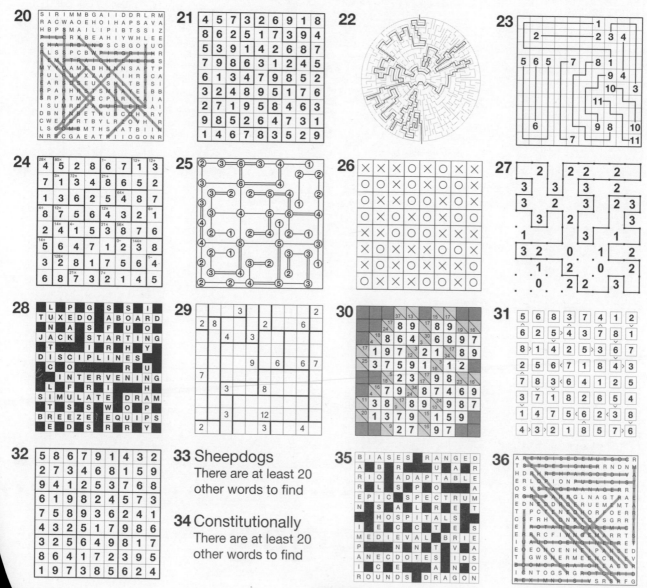

20

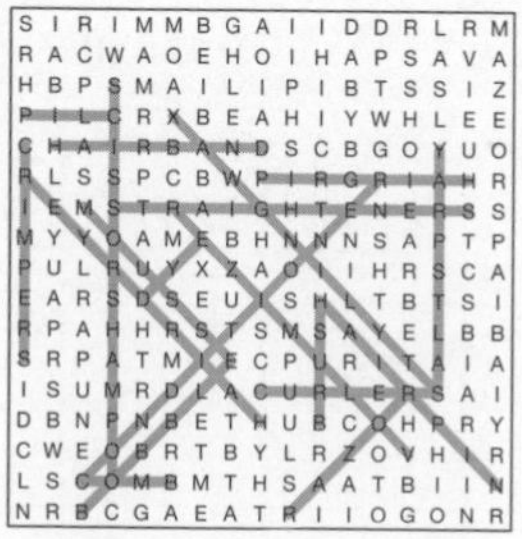

21

4	5	7	3	2	6	9	1	8
8	6	2	5	1	7	3	9	4
5	3	9	1	4	2	6	8	7
7	9	8	6	3	1	2	4	5
6	1	3	4	7	9	8	5	2
3	2	4	8	9	5	1	7	6
2	7	1	9	5	8	4	6	3
9	8	5	2	6	4	7	3	1
1	4	6	7	8	3	5	2	9

22

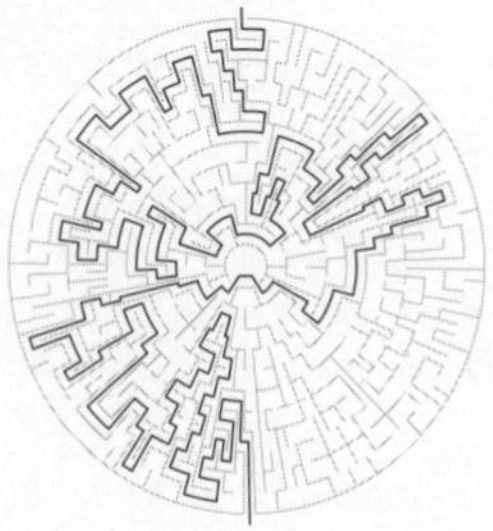

23

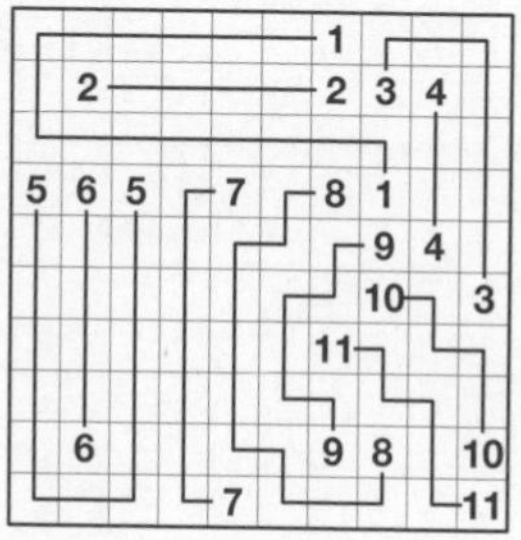

24

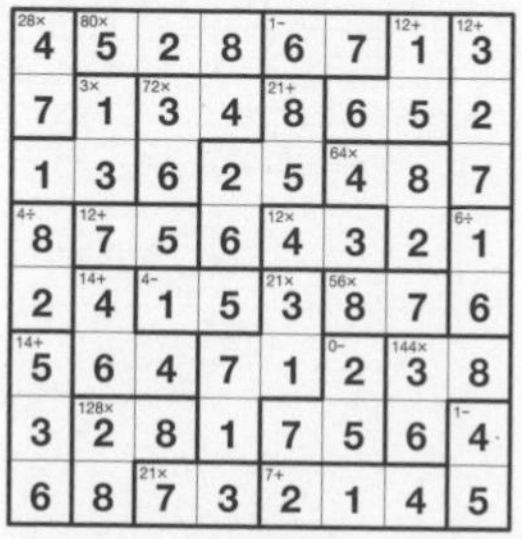

25

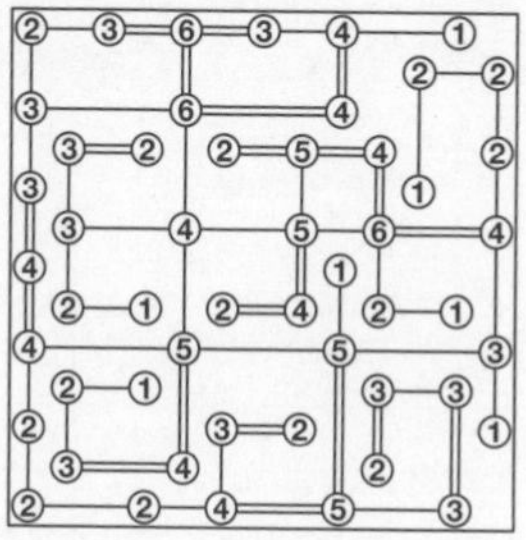

26

X	X	X	O	X	O	X	X
O	O	X	O	X	O	O	X
O	X	X	O	O	X	O	X
O	X	O	X	O	X	O	O
X	X	O	O	O	X	X	X
X	O	X	X	X	O	O	X
X	O	X	O	X	X	X	O
O	X	O	X	O	O	X	O

27

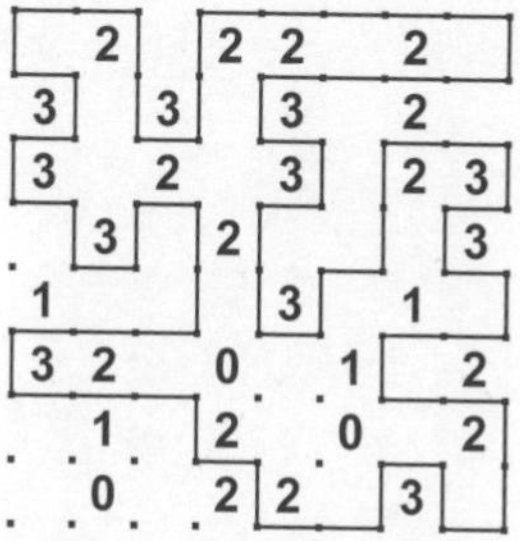

28

29

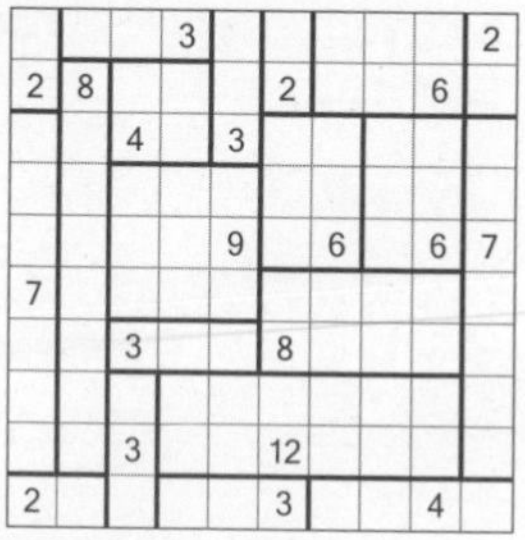

30

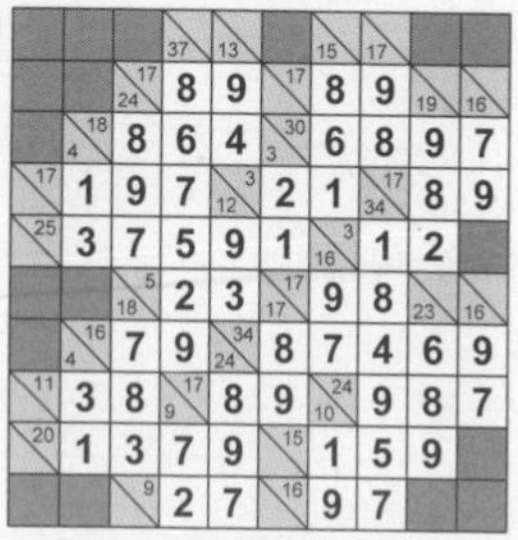

31

32

5	8	6	7	9	1	4	3	2
2	7	3	4	6	8	1	5	9
9	4	1	2	5	3	7	6	8
6	1	9	8	2	4	5	7	3
7	5	8	9	3	6	2	4	1
4	3	2	5	1	7	9	8	6
3	2	5	6	4	9	8	1	7
8	6	4	1	7	2	3	9	5
1	9	7	3	8	5	6	2	4

33 Sheepdogs
There are at least 20 other words to find

34 Constitutionally
There are at least 20 other words to find

35

36

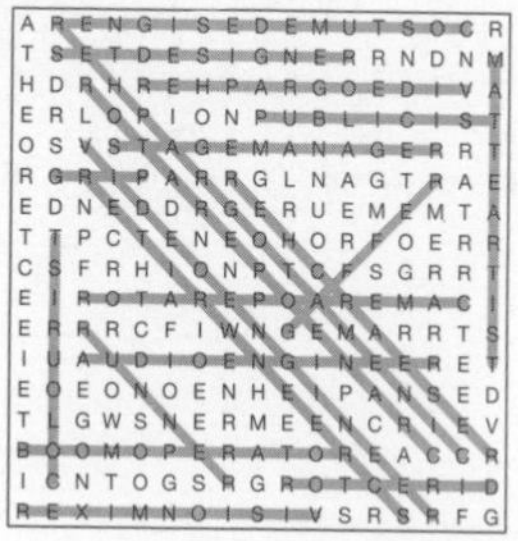

Solutions

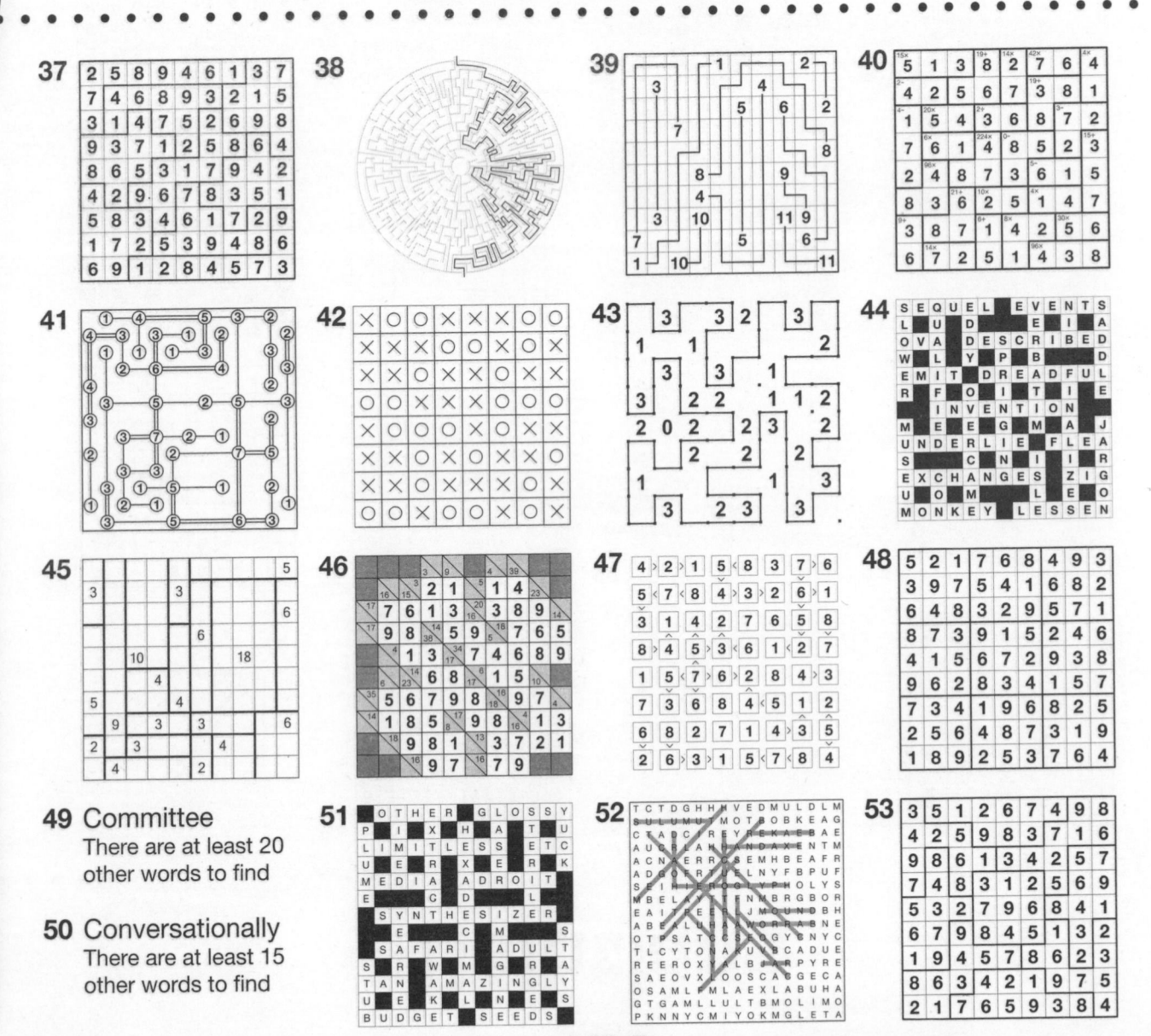

37

2	5	8	9	4	6	1	3	7
7	4	6	8	9	3	2	1	5
3	1	4	7	5	2	6	9	8
9	3	7	1	2	5	8	6	4
8	6	5	3	1	7	9	4	2
4	2	9	6	7	8	3	5	1
5	8	3	4	6	1	7	2	9
1	7	2	5	3	9	4	8	6
6	9	1	2	8	4	5	7	3

38

39

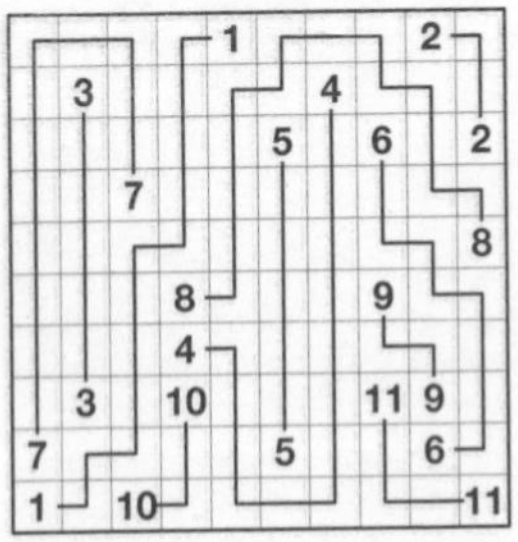

40

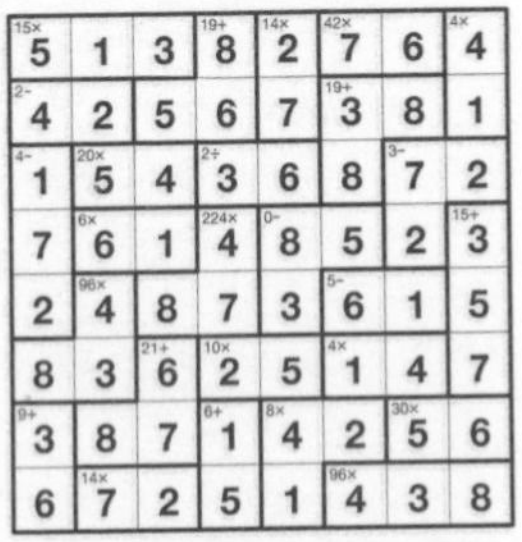

41

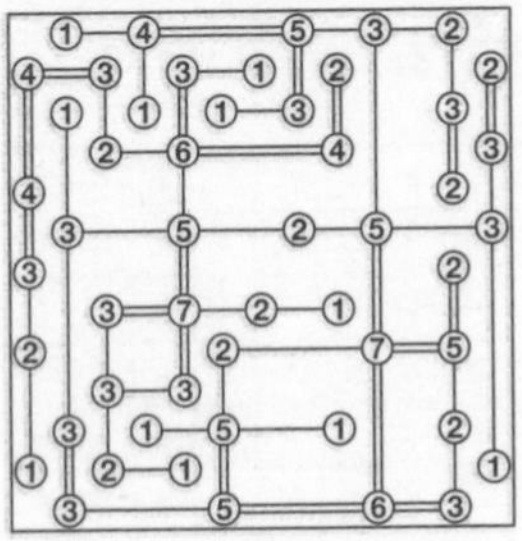

42

X	O	O	X	X	X	O	O
X	X	X	O	O	X	O	X
X	X	O	X	X	O	X	X
O	O	X	X	X	O	O	O
X	O	O	O	X	O	X	X
X	X	O	X	O	X	X	O
X	X	O	X	X	X	O	X
O	O	X	O	O	X	O	X

43

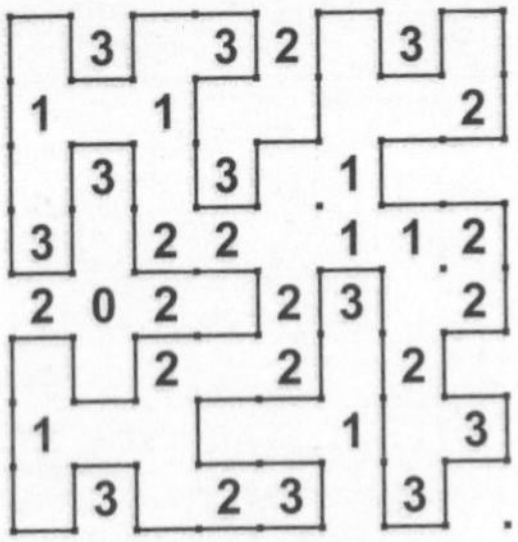

44

45

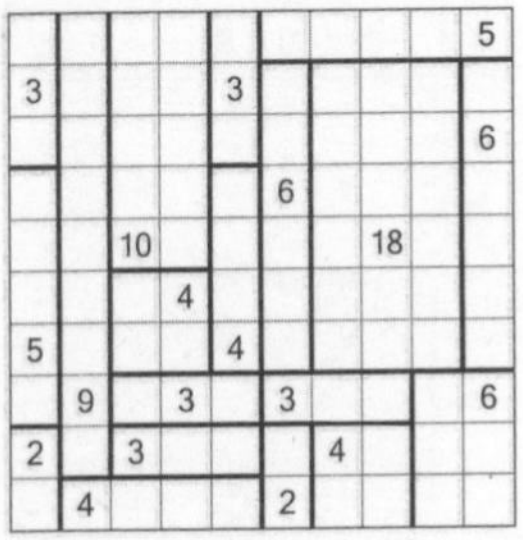

46

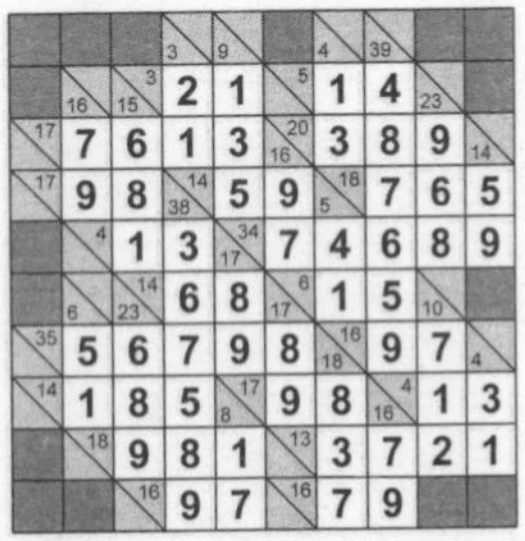

47

48

5	2	1	7	6	8	4	9	3
3	9	7	5	4	1	6	8	2
6	4	8	3	2	9	5	7	1
8	7	3	9	1	5	2	4	6
4	1	5	6	7	2	9	3	8
9	6	2	8	3	4	1	5	7
7	3	4	1	9	6	8	2	5
2	5	6	4	8	7	3	1	9
1	8	9	2	5	3	7	6	4

49 Committee
There are at least 20 other words to find

50 Conversationally
There are at least 15 other words to find

51

52

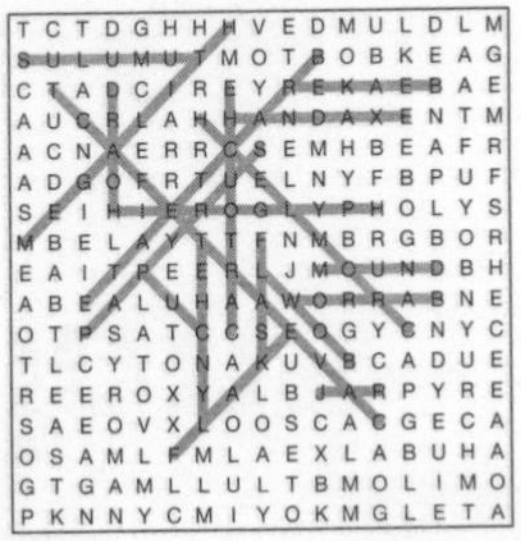

53

3	5	1	2	6	7	4	9	8
4	2	5	9	8	3	7	1	6
9	8	6	1	3	4	2	5	7
7	4	8	3	1	2	5	6	9
5	3	2	7	9	6	8	4	1
6	7	9	8	4	5	1	3	2
1	9	4	5	7	8	6	2	3
8	6	3	4	2	1	9	7	5
2	1	7	6	5	9	3	8	4

Solutions

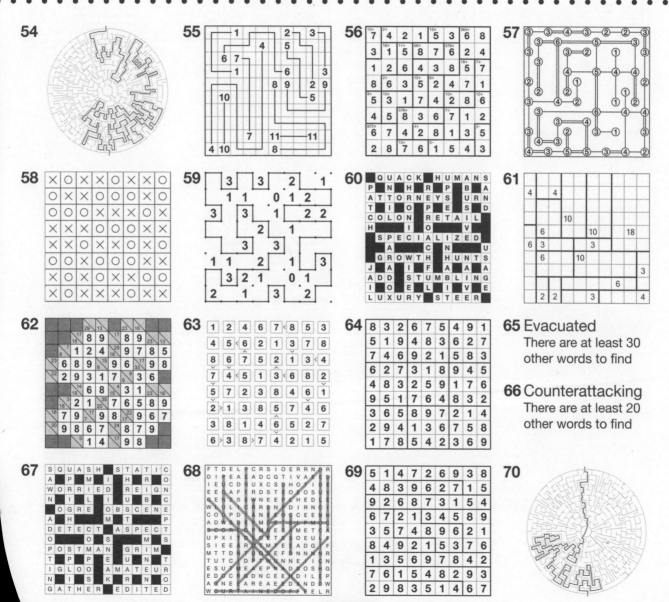

54

55

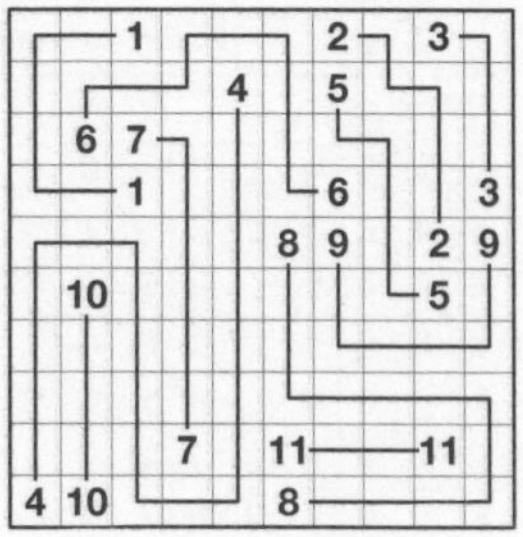

56

10+ 7	2÷ 4	2	1	15× 5	3	384× 6	8
3	16× 1	11+ 5	56× 8	7	576× 6	2	4
1	2	6	4	3	8	16+ 5	7× 7
8	2÷ 6	3	12+ 5	6+ 2	4	7	1
9+ 5	15× 3	1	7	4	10+ 2	8	12+ 6
4	5	576× 8	3	6	7÷ 7	1	2
672× 6	7	4	4÷ 2	8	1	3	2− 5
2	8	13+ 7	6	0− 1	5	4	3

57

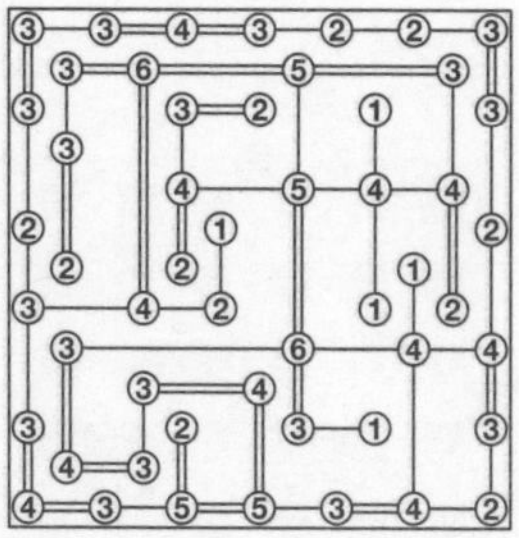

58

X	O	X	X	O	X	X	O
O	X	X	O	O	O	X	O
O	O	O	X	X	X	O	X
X	X	X	O	O	O	X	X
X	X	O	X	X	O	X	O
O	O	X	O	O	O	X	X
X	O	X	O	X	X	O	O
X	O	X	X	X	O	X	X

59

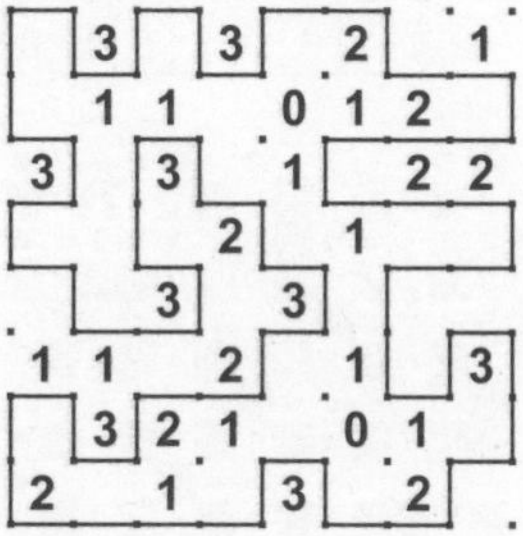

60

■	Q	U	A	C	K	■	H	U	M	A	N	S
P	■	N	■	H	■	R	■	P	■	B	■	A
A	T	T	O	R	N	E	Y	S	■	U	R	N
T	■	I	■	O	■	P	■	E	■	S	■	D
C	O	L	O	N	■	R	E	T	A	I	L	■
H	■	■	■	I	■	O	■	■	■	V	■	■
■	S	P	E	C	I	A	L	I	Z	E	D	■
■	■	A	■	■	■	C	■	N	■	■	■	U
■	G	R	O	W	T	H	■	H	U	N	T	S
J	■	A	■	I	■	F	■	A	■	A	■	A
A	D	D	■	S	T	U	M	B	L	I	N	G
I	■	O	■	E	■	L	■	I	■	V	■	E
L	U	X	U	R	Y	■	S	T	E	E	R	■

61

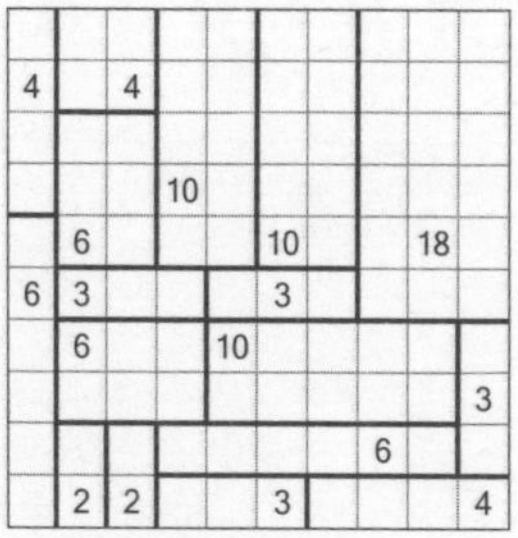

62

63

1	2	4	6	7	8	5	3
4	5	6	2	1	3	7	8
8	6	7	5	2	1	3	4
7	4	5	1	3	6	8	2
5	7	2	3	8	4	6	1
2	1	3	8	5	7	4	6
3	8	1	4	6	5	2	7
6	3	8	7	4	2	1	5

64

8	3	2	6	7	5	4	9	1
5	1	9	4	8	3	6	2	7
7	4	6	9	2	1	5	8	3
6	2	7	3	1	8	9	4	5
4	8	3	2	5	9	1	7	6
9	5	1	7	6	4	8	3	2
3	6	5	8	9	7	2	1	4
2	9	4	1	3	6	7	5	8
1	7	8	5	4	2	3	6	9

65 Evacuated
There are at least 30 other words to find

66 Counterattacking
There are at least 20 other words to find

67

S	Q	U	A	S	H	■	S	T	A	T	I	C
A	■	P	■	M	■	I	■	H	■	R	■	O
W	O	R	R	I	E	D	■	R	E	I	G	N
N	■	I	■	L	■	I	■	U	■	B	■	C
■	O	G	R	E	■	O	B	S	C	E	N	E
A	■	H	■	■	■	M	■	T	■	■	■	P
D	E	T	E	C	T	■	A	S	P	E	C	T
O	■	■	■	O	■	S	■	■	■	M	■	S
P	O	S	T	M	A	N	■	G	R	I	M	■
T	■	P	■	P	■	E	■	U	■	N	■	T
I	G	L	O	O	■	A	M	A	T	E	U	R
N	■	I	■	S	■	K	■	R	■	N	■	O
G	A	T	H	E	R	■	E	D	I	T	E	D

68

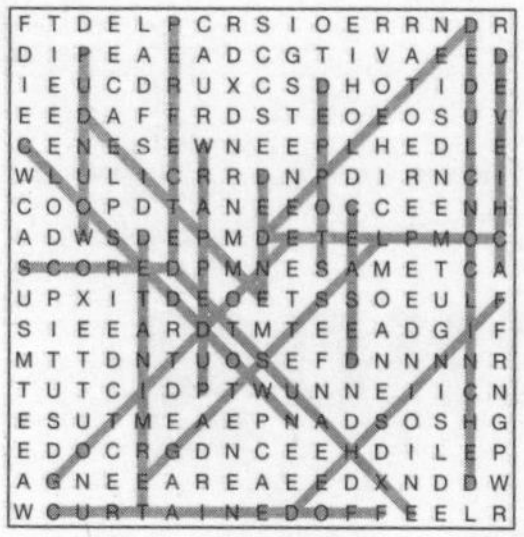

69

5	1	4	7	2	6	9	3	8
4	8	3	9	6	2	7	1	5
9	2	6	8	7	3	1	5	4
6	7	2	1	3	4	5	8	9
3	5	7	4	8	9	6	2	1
8	4	9	2	1	5	3	7	6
1	3	5	6	9	7	8	4	2
7	6	1	5	4	8	2	9	3
2	9	8	3	5	1	4	6	7

70

Solutions

71

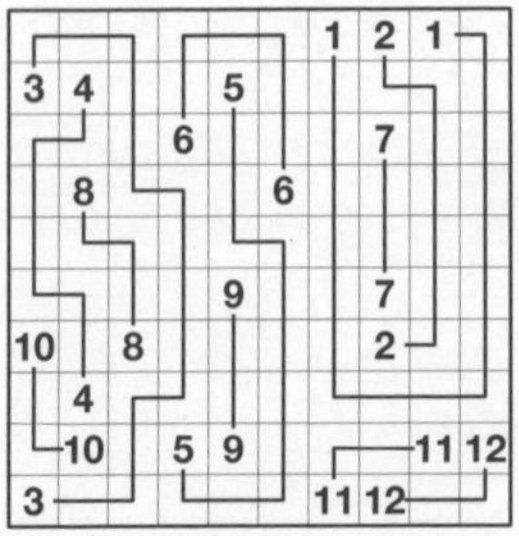

72

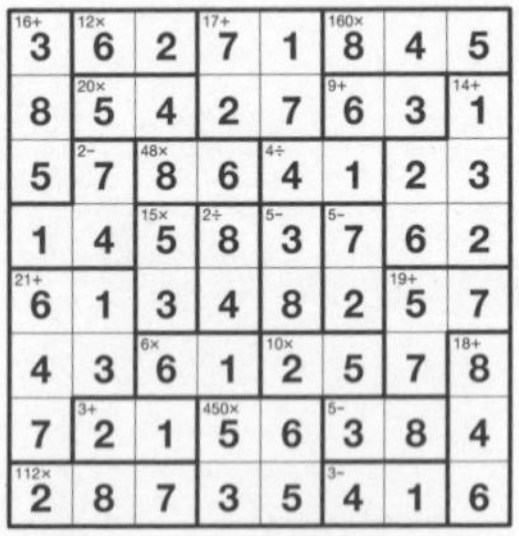

73

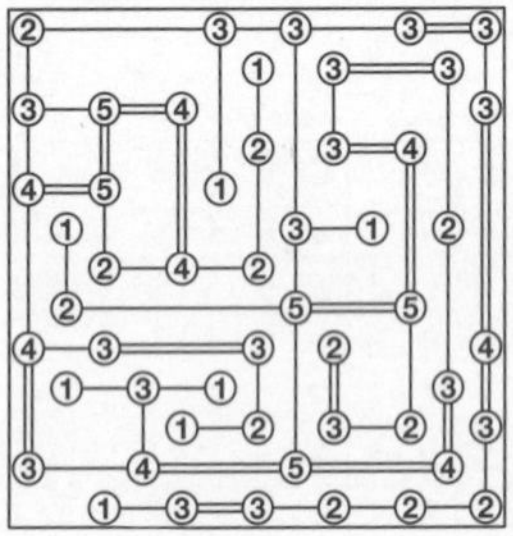

74

O	O	O	X	X	X	O	O
X	O	O	O	X	O	X	X
X	O	X	O	O	X	O	O
O	X	O	X	X	X	O	X
O	X	O	O	O	X	O	O
O	O	X	X	X	O	X	X
X	O	O	O	X	X	O	O
O	O	X	X	O	O	X	X

75

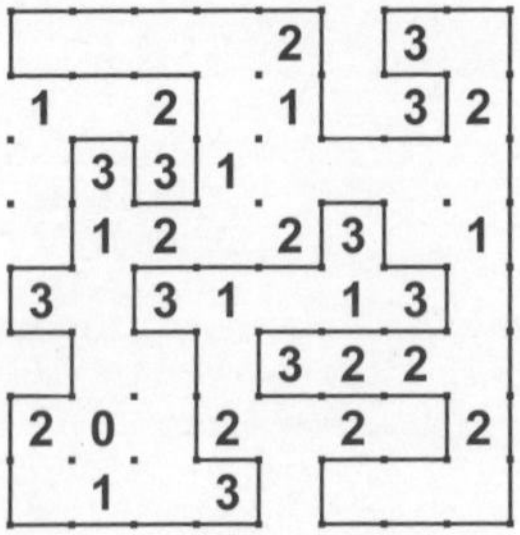

76

77

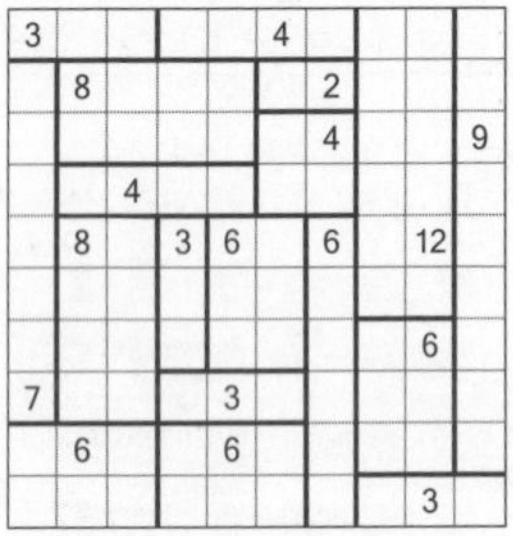

78

79

80

3	4	9	7	6	8	2	1	5
8	6	5	1	9	2	7	3	4
2	1	7	4	5	3	6	9	8
7	5	2	6	1	9	4	8	3
6	8	4	3	2	5	9	7	1
1	9	3	8	4	7	5	6	2
5	3	8	9	7	4	1	2	6
4	7	6	2	8	1	3	5	9
9	2	1	5	3	6	8	4	7

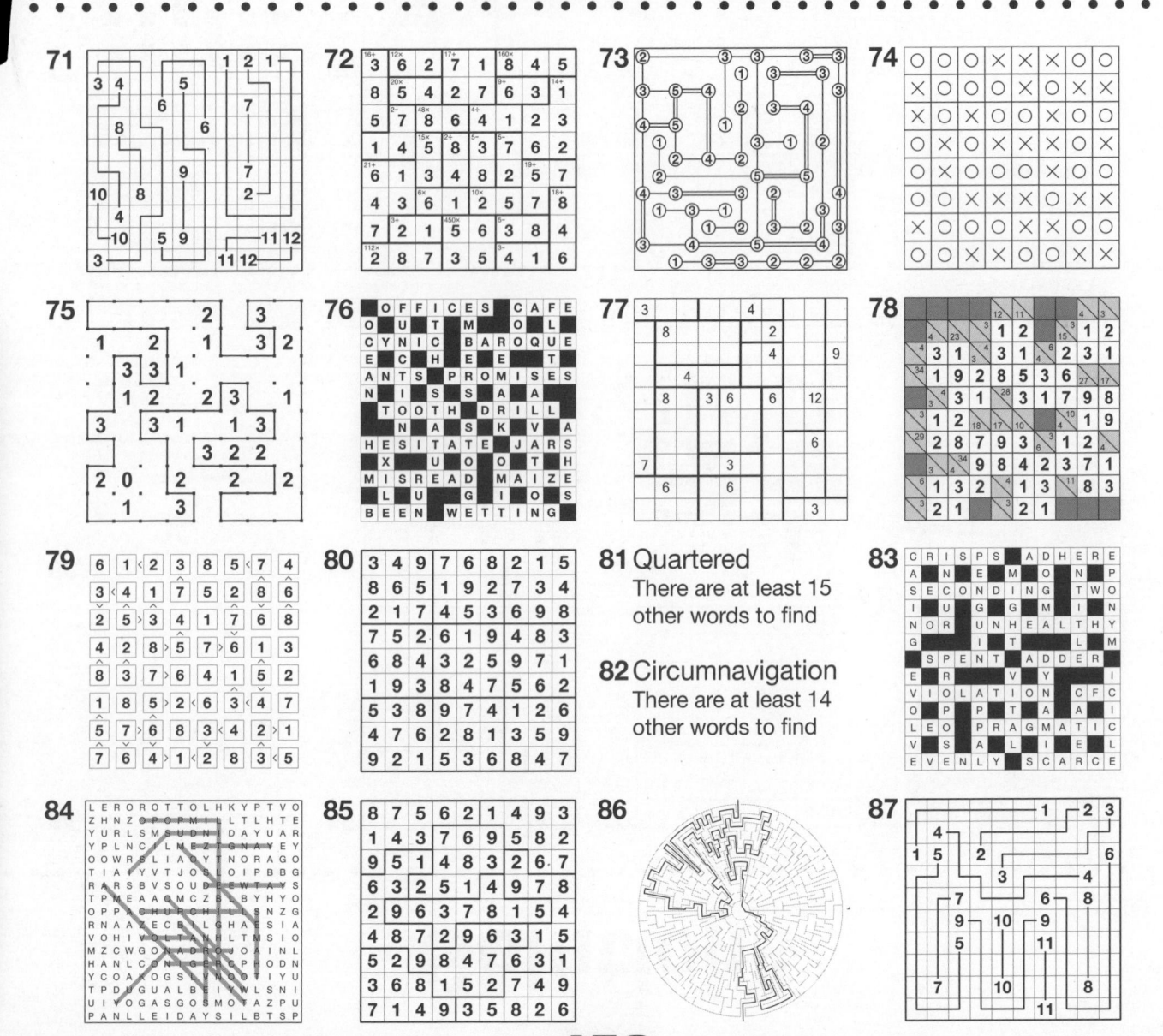

81 Quartered
There are at least 15 other words to find

82 Circumnavigation
There are at least 14 other words to find

83

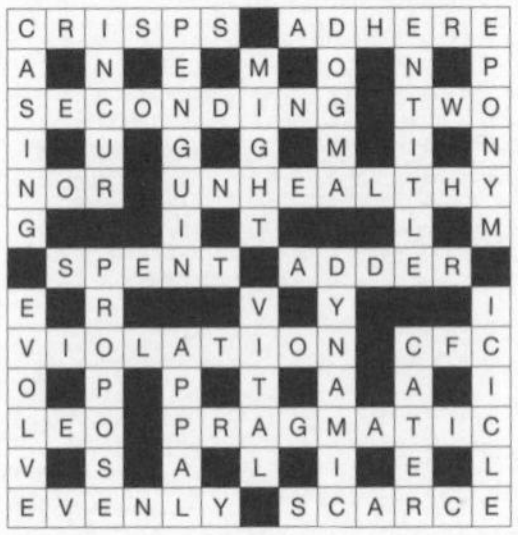

84

85

8	7	5	6	2	1	4	9	3
1	4	3	7	6	9	5	8	2
9	5	1	4	8	3	2	6	7
6	3	2	5	1	4	9	7	8
2	9	6	3	7	8	1	5	4
4	8	7	2	9	6	3	1	5
5	2	9	8	4	7	6	3	1
3	6	8	1	5	2	7	4	9
7	1	4	9	3	5	8	2	6

86

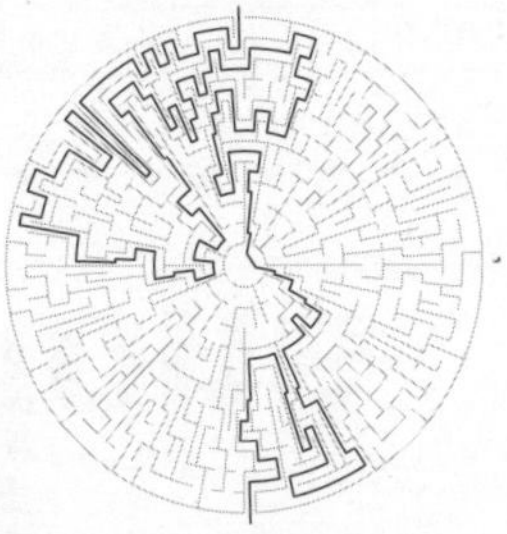

87

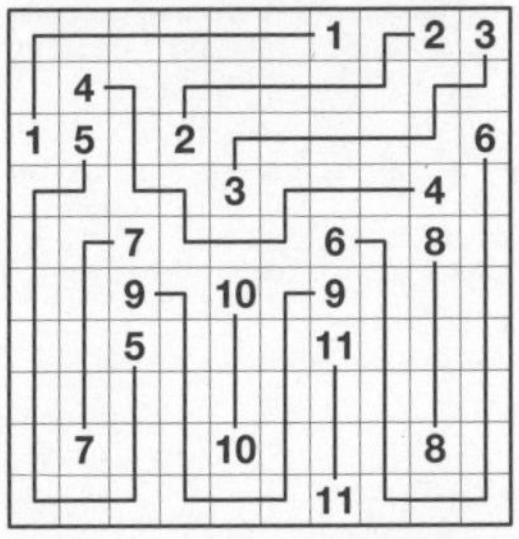

Solutions

88

1	4	6	5	7	3	8	2
2	6	4	8	1	7	3	5
4	7	3	1	5	2	6	8
3	2	7	4	6	8	5	1
8	5	2	6	4	1	7	3
7	3	5	2	8	6	1	4
5	1	8	7	3	4	2	6
6	8	1	3	2	5	4	7

89

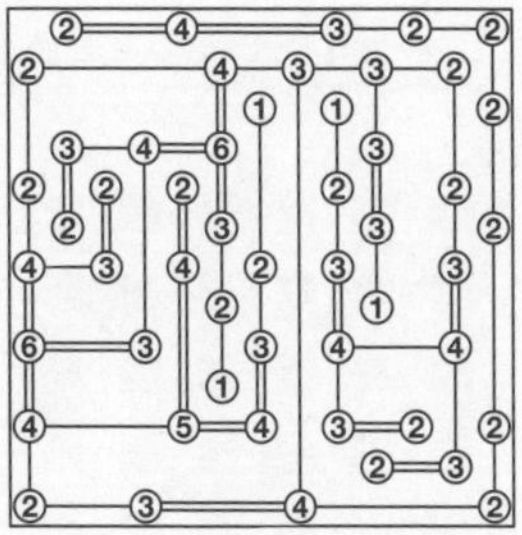

90

O	X	O	X	O	X	O	X
X	X	O	O	X	O	X	O
X	O	X	O	X	O	X	X
O	X	O	X	X	X	O	X
O	X	O	O	O	X	O	O
O	O	O	X	X	X	O	O
X	O	X	X	X	O	X	O
X	O	O	X	X	O	O	X

91

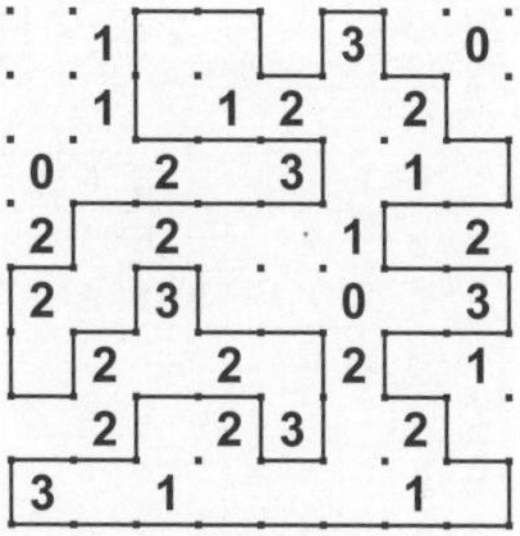

92

	M	O	D	U	L	E	S		A	B	E	T
G		T		R		X		A		A		A
E	X	H	I	B	I	T		C	A	N	A	L
T		E		A		E		Q		D		K
A	P	R	O	N		N	E	U	R	A	L	
W				I		T		A		N		R
A	B	L	A	Z	E		D	I	L	A	T	E
Y		E		A		S		N				V
	B	A	T	T	L	E		T	E	P	E	E
J		F		I		R		A		R		N
I	G	L	O	O		V	E	N	D	I	N	G
V		E		N		E		C		N		E
E	A	T	S		A	S	P	E	C	T	S	

93

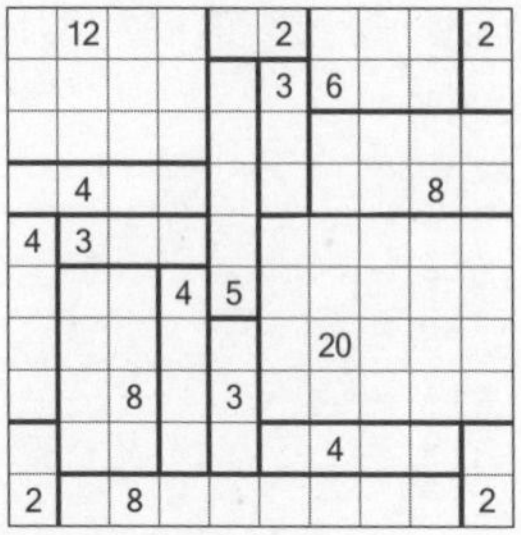

94

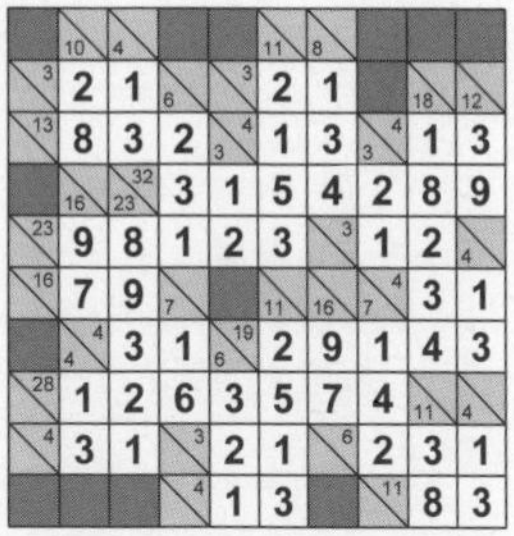

95

7	4	6	1	5	3	2	8
3	7	1	5	8	2	4	6
6	1	8	2	4	5	3	7
1	2	4	6	3	8	7	5
2	3	5	4	7	6	8	1
8	6	3	7	1	4	5	2
5	8	7	3	2	1	6	4
4	5	2	8	6	7	1	3

96

6	5	4	3	1	9	8	2	7
9	1	7	2	8	4	6	3	5
8	2	3	5	7	6	9	1	4
2	8	9	4	6	3	5	7	1
1	4	5	7	9	8	3	6	2
7	3	6	1	2	5	4	9	8
5	6	2	8	3	7	1	4	9
4	9	1	6	5	2	7	8	3
3	7	8	9	4	1	2	5	6

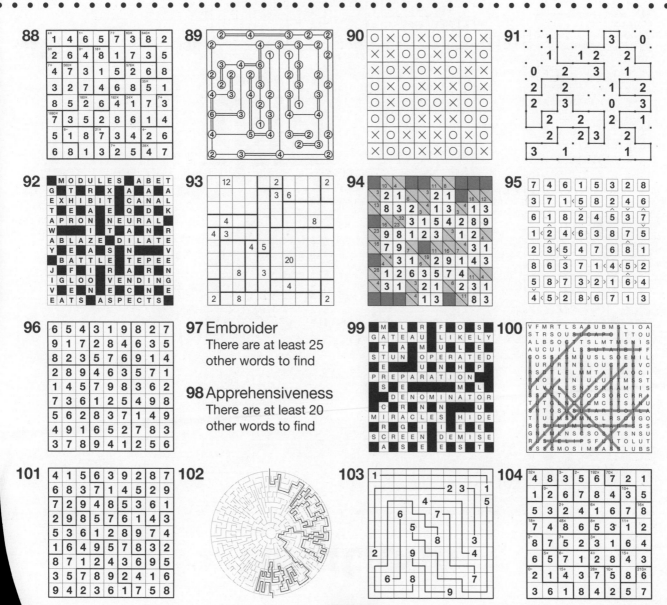

97 Embroider
There are at least 25 other words to find

98 Apprehensiveness
There are at least 20 other words to find

99

	M		L		R		F		O		S	
G	A	T	E	A	U		L	I	K	E	L	Y
	T		A		M		U		L		E	
S	T	U	N		O	P	E	R	A	T	E	D
	E				U		N		H		P	
P	R	E	P	A	R	A	T	I	O	N		
	S		E						M		L	
		D	E	N	O	M	I	N	A	T	O	R
	C		R		N		N				U	
M	I	R	A	C	L	E	S		H	I	D	E
	R		G		I		I		E		E	
S	C	R	E	E	N		D	E	M	I	S	E
	A		S		E		E		S		T	

100

101

4	1	5	6	3	9	2	8	7
6	8	3	7	1	4	5	2	9
7	2	9	4	8	5	3	6	1
2	9	8	5	7	6	1	4	3
5	3	6	1	2	8	9	7	4
1	6	4	9	5	7	8	3	2
8	7	1	2	4	3	6	9	5
3	5	7	8	9	2	4	1	6
9	4	2	3	6	1	7	5	8

102

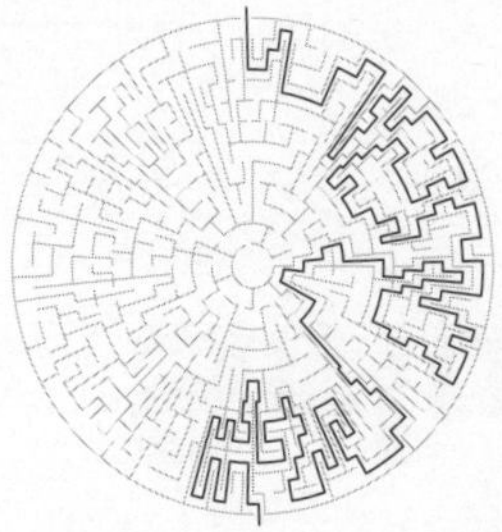

103

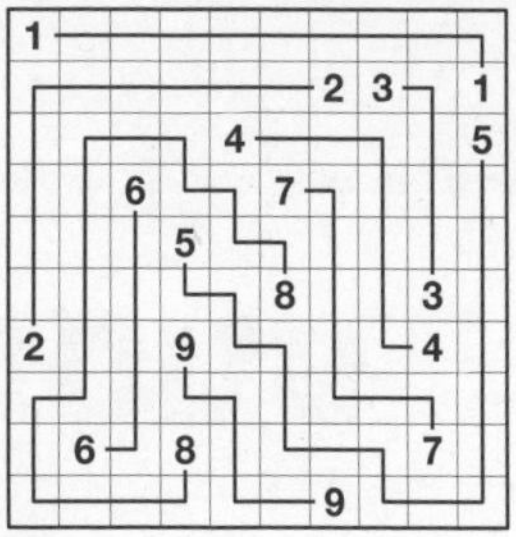

104

4	8	3	5	6	7	2	1
1	2	6	7	8	4	3	5
5	3	2	4	1	6	7	8
7	4	8	6	5	3	1	2
8	7	5	2	3	1	6	4
6	5	7	1	2	8	4	3
2	1	4	3	7	5	8	6
3	6	1	8	4	2	5	7

Solutions

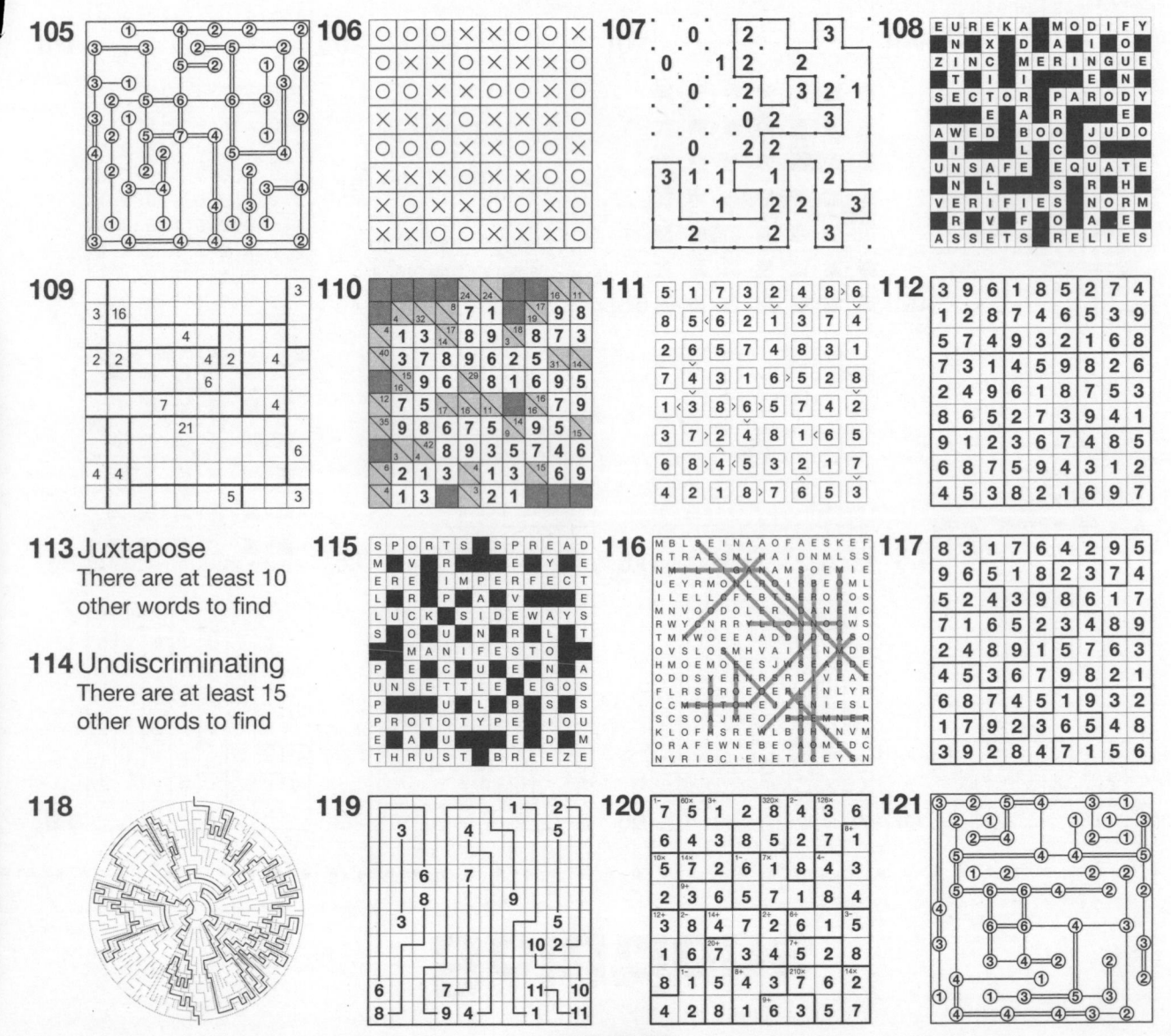

105

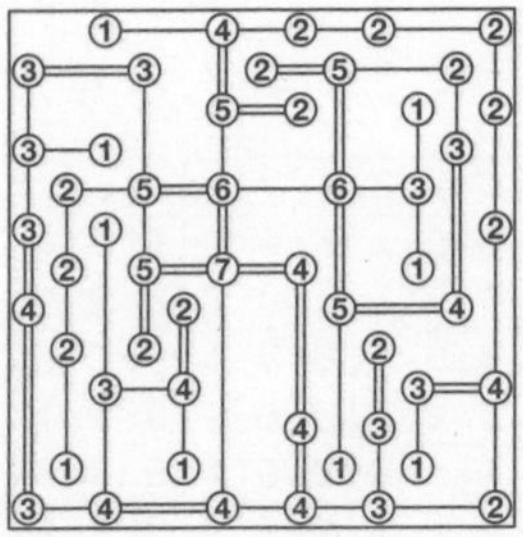

106

O	O	O	X	X	O	O	X
O	X	X	O	X	X	X	O
O	O	X	X	O	O	X	O
X	X	X	O	X	X	X	O
O	O	O	X	X	O	O	X
X	X	X	O	X	X	O	O
X	O	X	X	O	O	X	O
X	X	O	O	X	X	X	O

107

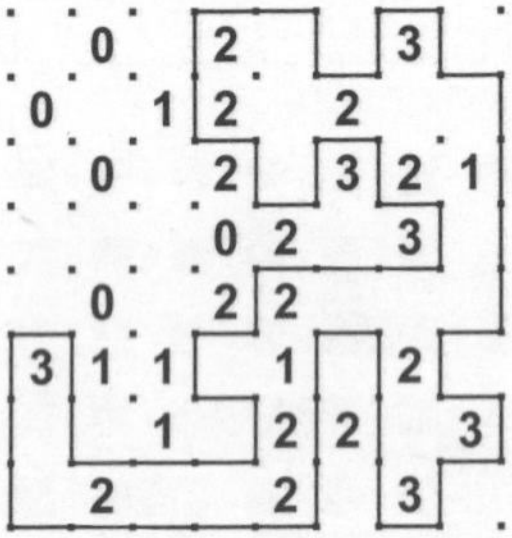

108

109

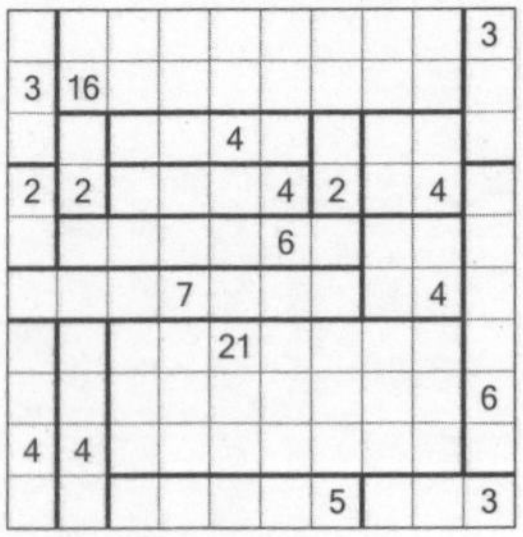

110

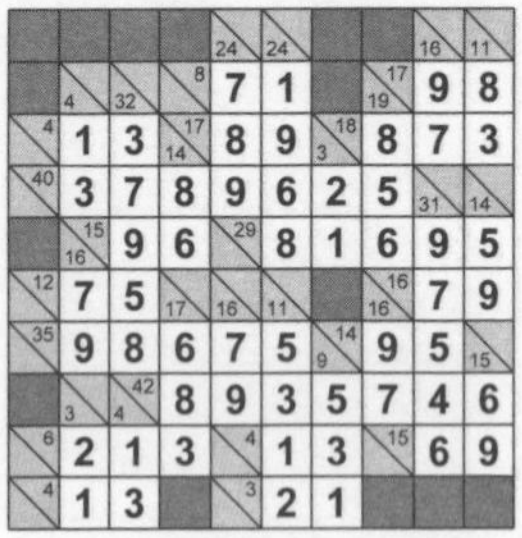

111

112

3	9	6	1	8	5	2	7	4
1	2	8	7	4	6	5	3	9
5	7	4	9	3	2	1	6	8
7	3	1	4	5	9	8	2	6
2	4	9	6	1	8	7	5	3
8	6	5	2	7	3	9	4	1
9	1	2	3	6	7	4	8	5
6	8	7	5	9	4	3	1	2
4	5	3	8	2	1	6	9	7

113 Juxtapose
There are at least 10 other words to find

114 Undiscriminating
There are at least 15 other words to find

115

116

117

8	3	1	7	6	4	2	9	5
9	6	5	1	8	2	3	7	4
5	2	4	3	9	8	6	1	7
7	1	6	5	2	3	4	8	9
2	4	8	9	1	5	7	6	3
4	5	3	6	7	9	8	2	1
6	8	7	4	5	1	9	3	2
1	7	9	2	3	6	5	4	8
3	9	2	8	4	7	1	5	6

118

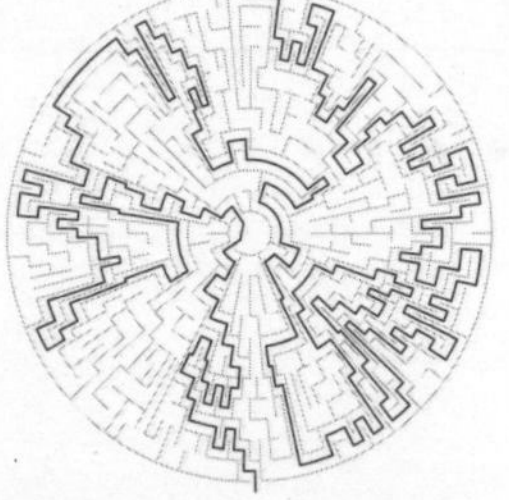

119

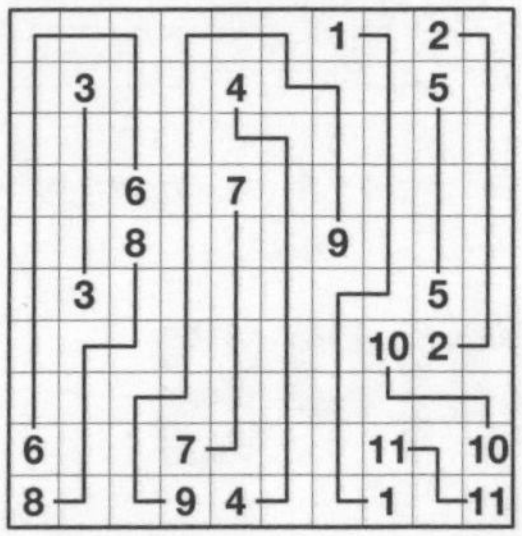

120

121

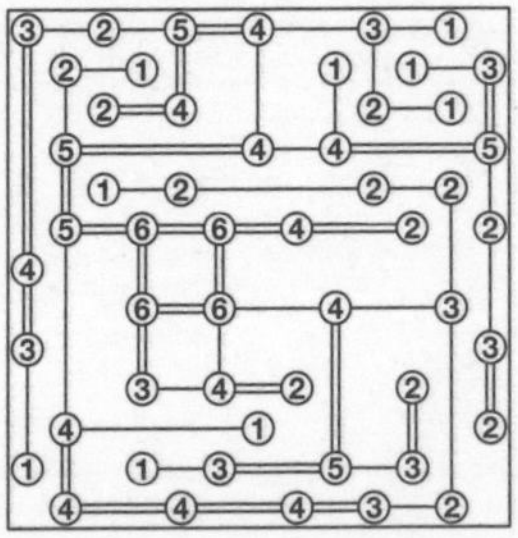

Solutions

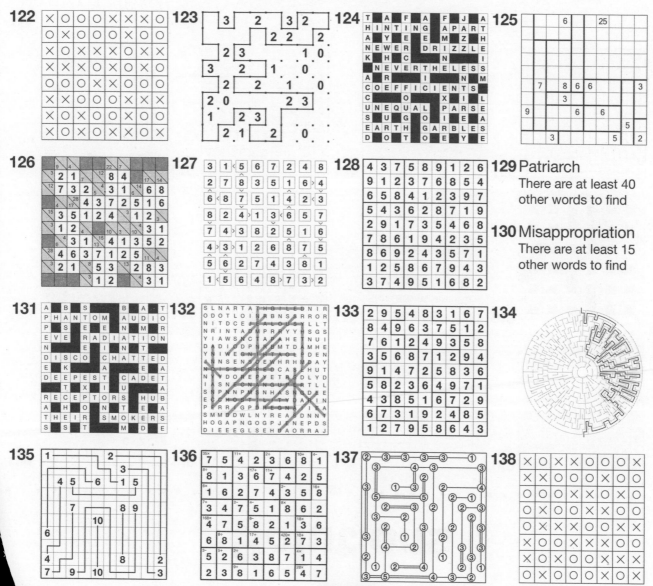

122

X	O	O	O	X	X	X	O
O	X	O	O	O	X	O	O
X	O	X	X	X	O	X	X
X	X	X	O	X	O	X	O
O	O	O	X	X	O	O	O
X	X	O	O	O	X	X	X
X	O	X	O	O	X	O	O
X	O	X	O	X	X	O	X

123

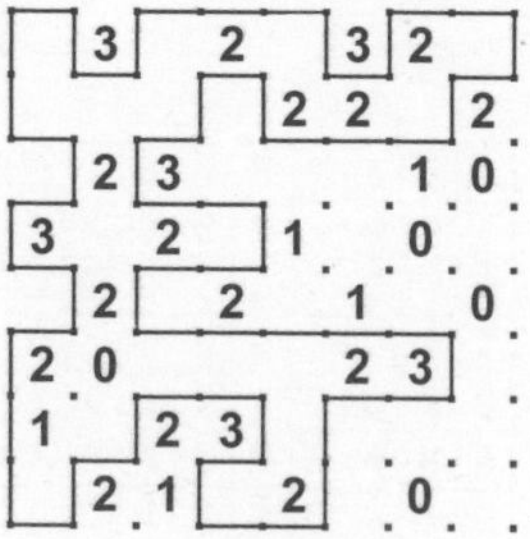

124

125

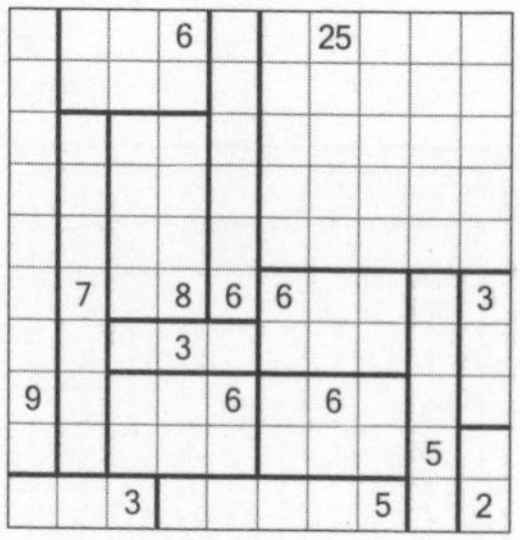

126

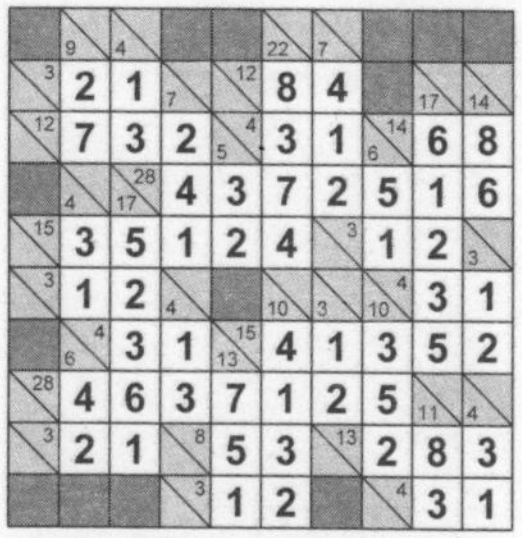

127

128

4	3	7	5	8	9	1	2	6
9	1	2	3	7	6	8	5	4
6	5	8	4	1	2	3	9	7
5	4	3	6	2	8	7	1	9
2	9	1	7	3	5	4	6	8
7	8	6	1	9	4	2	3	5
8	6	9	2	4	3	5	7	1
1	2	5	8	6	7	9	4	3
3	7	4	9	5	1	6	8	2

129 Patriarch

There are at least 40 other words to find

130 Misappropriation

There are at least 15 other words to find

131

132

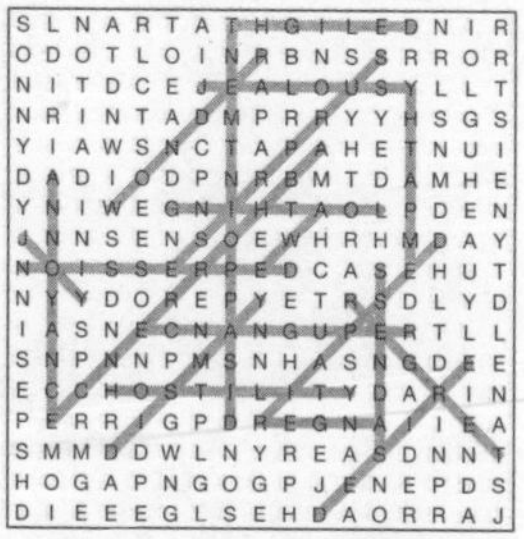

133

2	9	5	4	8	3	1	6	7
8	4	9	6	3	7	5	1	2
7	6	1	2	4	9	3	5	8
3	5	6	8	7	1	2	9	4
9	1	4	7	2	5	8	3	6
5	8	2	3	6	4	9	7	1
4	3	8	5	1	6	7	2	9
6	7	3	1	9	2	4	8	5
1	2	7	9	5	8	6	4	3

134

135

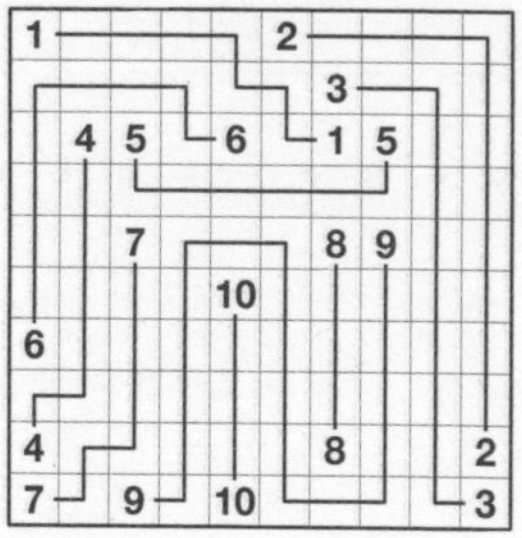

136

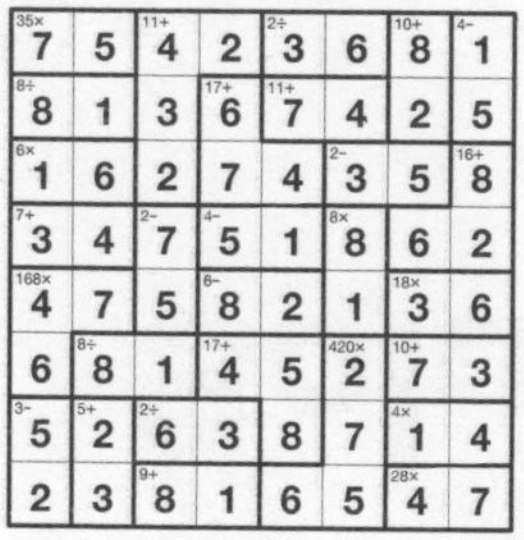

137

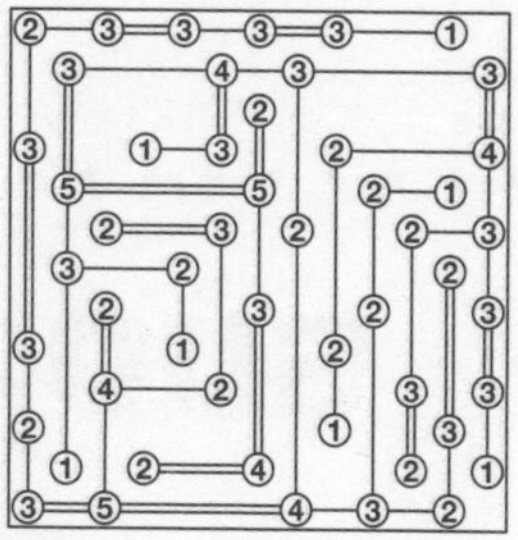

138

X	O	X	X	O	O	O	X
X	X	O	O	O	X	O	O
O	O	O	X	X	O	X	O
O	X	O	O	X	X	O	O
O	X	X	X	O	O	X	X
X	O	O	X	X	X	O	O
X	O	X	O	O	X	X	X
O	X	O	O	O	X	O	X

Solutions

139
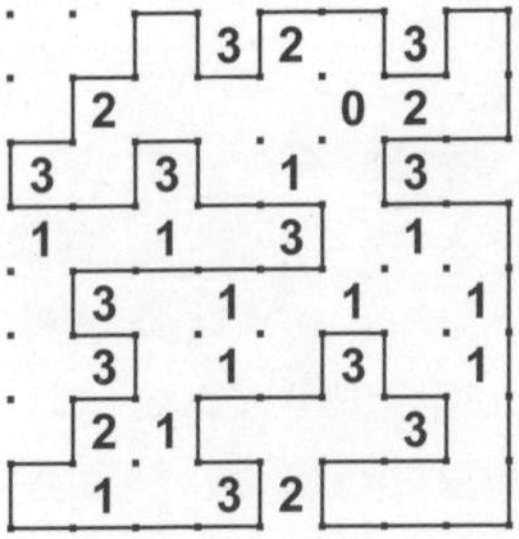

140

141
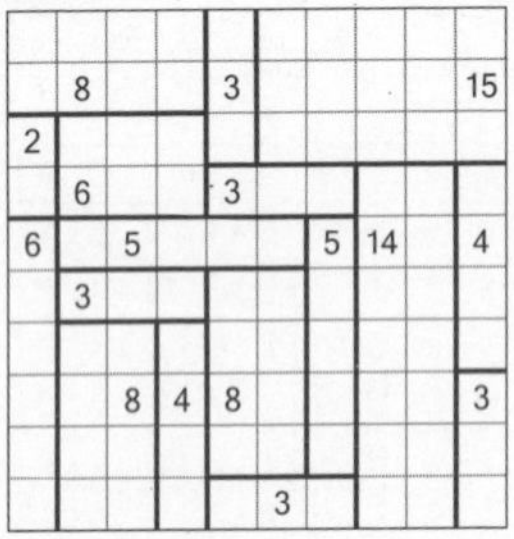

142

143

144

1	9	6	7	8	2	4	3	5
4	3	7	5	1	6	8	9	2
5	8	2	9	4	3	7	1	6
8	5	4	3	7	1	6	2	9
3	6	9	2	5	4	1	7	8
7	2	1	6	9	8	3	5	4
2	1	3	8	6	5	9	4	7
6	7	5	4	3	9	2	8	1
9	4	8	1	2	7	5	6	3

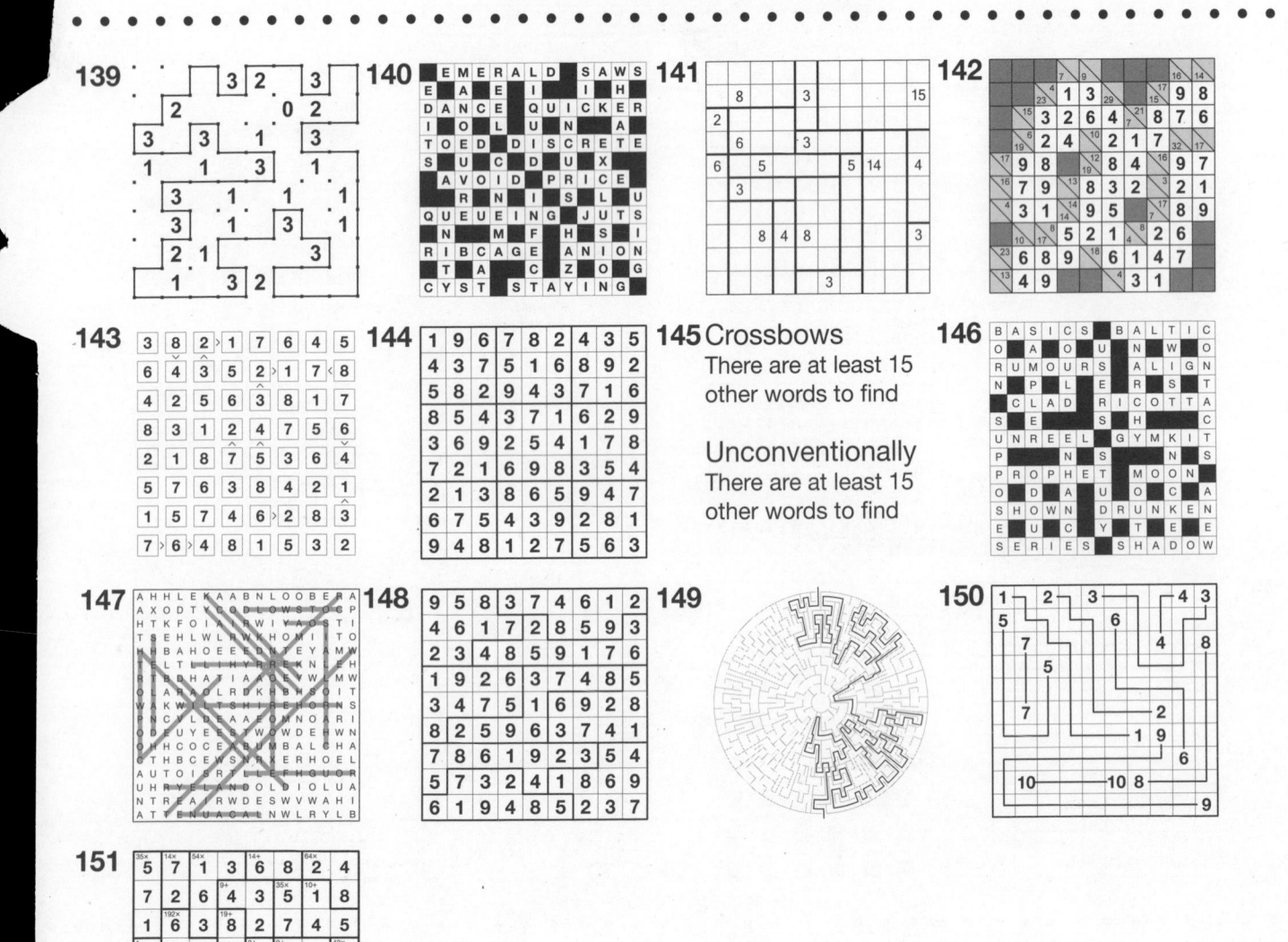

145 Crossbows
There are at least 15 other words to find

Unconventionally
There are at least 15 other words to find

146

147

148

9	5	8	3	7	4	6	1	2
4	6	1	7	2	8	5	9	3
2	3	4	8	5	9	1	7	6
1	9	2	6	3	7	4	8	5
3	4	7	5	1	6	9	2	8
8	2	5	9	6	3	7	4	1
7	8	6	1	9	2	3	5	4
5	7	3	2	4	1	8	6	9
6	1	9	4	8	5	2	3	7

149

150
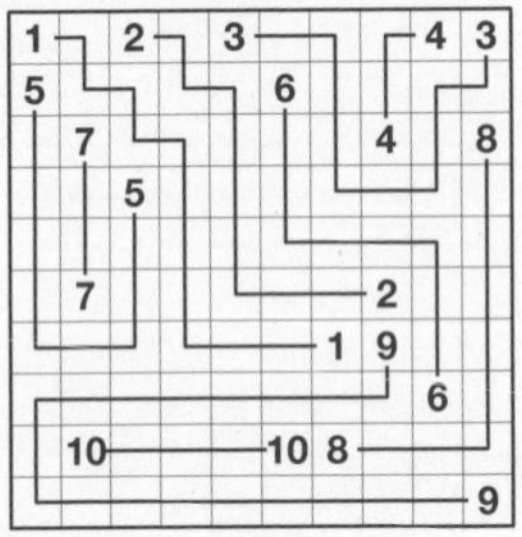

151